"Not all of us have your confidence!"

His eyes gleamed at her as he answered. "*You* should have stacks of it. You're not a bad-looking girl."

"Thanks."

Head on one side, he surveyed her. "You're a bit too thin for some people's taste, but you appeal to mine. And you have an extremely kissable mouth."

Quickly Amanda drew back, but not quickly enough. His arms came tightly around her. "Very kissable," he repeated, and proceeded to prove the point.

Red Clark's manner might be casual, but he took his kissing seriously. Here was passion and intensity, and Amanda felt herself responding. Aware of it, he drew her closer still.

"It seems you're an expert at making love," she finally said.

"You don't know the half of it," he said. "But you will!"

RACHEL LINDSAY
is also the author of these

Harlequin Presents

and these

Harlequin Romances

RACHEL LINDSAY

food for love

Harlequin Books

TORONTO • LONDON • LOS ANGELES • AMSTERDAM
SYDNEY • HAMBURG • PARIS • STOCKHOLM • ATHENS • TOKYO

Harlequin Presents edition published December 1974
ISBN 0-373-15043-1

Second printing September 1977
Third printing October 1977
Fourth printing March 1979
Fifth printing June 1982

Original hardcover edition published in 1974
by Mills & Boon Limited

CHAPTER ONE

'FEELING bitter about your father's death won't help you or your mother to get over it,' Mr. Treadmarsh told Amanda Stewart. 'There's nothing worse than bitterness for making grief linger.'

'I can't help my feelings,' Amanda said. 'When I think what Homefare did to him.... They as good as caused his death!'

'If it hadn't been them it would have been another supermarket group,' Mr. Treadmarsh replied. 'Much as you and I may regret it, the day of the small shop is doomed.'

'I know,' Amanda said bitterly. 'Supermarkets today and hypermarkets tomorrow. Where will it end?'

'With the death of the small shopkeeper.' Mr. Treadmarsh looked disconcerted as he realised what he had said. 'I'm sorry—I didn't mean——'

'That's all right.' Amanda swallowed painfully, the thought of her father's death still too close for her to pretend she was not shattered by it. 'He was so young to die,' she burst out. 'Only sixty. The same age as my mother, and now she has no one.'

'She has you.'

'That isn't the same.'

'What are your plans?'

'I don't know. Money will be a problem, of course.'

'Your mother will get your father's Army pension. It won't keep her in luxury, but it should provide her with day-to-day necessities.' The elderly solicitor ruffled through the papers on his desk. 'I never understood why your father decided to go into the grocery business. I mean, it isn't the sort of thing one expected a retired Major to do. Market gardening now, but a grocery shop in a little village ...'

'It was much more than a shop, Mr. Treadmarsh. It was the hub of the village—a meeting place for everyone. You know what my father was like. Three months after he moved in he was Chairman of the Church Committee and Secretary of the Gardening Club. The village became his life. He would have done anything to preserve it. That's why he wouldn't sell out when Homefare made him their offer. He thought it was the thin end of the wedge, and that if one supermarket got in, others would follow.'

'I remember him coming to talk to me about it,' Mr. Treadmarsh vouchsafed. 'At the time I couldn't see why any large group would want to buy a village shop. I thought a thousand residents didn't warrant a supermarket.'

'They hadn't intended to open one at all,' Amanda explained. 'They wanted to buy Daddy out but let him remain in charge as manager. They made the same offer to several grocery shops in the district. My father was the only one who refused to sell. Then when they opened that huge hypermarket outside Brigford they closed down all the little shops they'd bought, and that forced everyone to go to the new place.'

'So even if your father had sold out to them and remained as manager, he'd have been out of a job in a couple of years?'

'Exactly. They paid their managers off very generously, though,' Amanda admitted, 'but my father was in a different position. He'd turned down Homefare's offer and then when he decided he'd have to sell to them, they laughed in his face.'

'It's understandable, I suppose,' Mr. Treadmarsh murmured. 'As I remember it, when they first approached your father their offer was generous. It's a pity he turned it down.'

'He believed the small shopkeeper should be encouraged, not destroyed.'

'A commendable belief, but not a logical one in this competitive age.' The solicitor peered at his papers again. 'You have a good job, I hope?'

'For the last year, since my mother's heart attack, I helped my father to run the shop.'

'Are you planning to keep it on?'

'There's nothing to keep on. It's been running at a loss for months. I'm sure it's the reason my father died. When Homefare wrote and said they wouldn't buy the shop at any price, he went for a walk to think things over. He crossed the street without looking and'—she clenched her hands but forced herself to go on—'and he was killed. Perhaps he didn't want to live. Perhaps death was the best way out for him.'

'Surely not.' Mr. Treadmarsh made no effort to hide his shock. 'Your father was still a comparatively young man, and he had his pension.'

'He'd been borrowing against it for more than a year. We owe the bank over two thousand pounds. We'll have to sell the cottage to pay it off.'

'And then what will you do?'

'Find a small flat in London. I'll get a better salary working there than if I stay in the country.'

Mr. Treadmarsh was still clucking his distress when Amanda left his office and walked down Brigford High Street. What a direct contrast these bright, brash shops were to the small village ones, where personal service

7

took the place of fluorescent lighting and home-made delicacies took the place of streamlined efficiency and cut-price produce. But it was the lower prices that people wanted these days. If this were not the case, her father would be alive today.

Driving home in the small car which she was not sure she could still afford to run, Amanda was far less confident of the future than she had given Mr. Treadmarsh to believe. But she did not have red hair for nothing: if there was any crying to be done she would do it alone. Indeed she dared not do it in front of her mother, whose health had failed alarmingly since her husband's death a month ago.

Because of this Amanda forced herself to look cheerful as she parked outside the village shop and walked through it into the cosy sitting-room at the back. Beyond it lay the garden and beyond this was the village green.

No wonder her parents had been enchanted when they had first come to Meredon Vale. Even now, seven years later, it was still picturesque and unspoiled, despite being only five miles from Brigford. She sighed; it was a pity the villagers hadn't shown her father the loyalty he had expected; had they done so, the shop could have remained a viable proposition. Not that he had ever blamed them for their behaviour; he had always insisted that his falling takings were a result of inflation and the financial squeeze, rather than his customers deserting him in favour of lower prices and the vast selection of the Homefare hypermarket.

'I've made you a cup of tea,' her mother said, coming from the small kitchen to greet her. 'I thought you'd need reviving after an afternoon with Mr. Treadmarsh!'

Gratefully Amanda took the cup. There was a similarity between the two women despite their difference in age. Both were tall and slim: Mrs. Stewart to the point of thinness, but Amanda fashionably so, with long slender arms and legs, a graceful neck supporting a delicate triangle of face and a creamy skin and dark blue eyes. Her hair came as a shock, however. Instead of the glossy brown one expected from such colouring, it was a vivid red. Thick and vibrant, it seemed to have a glowing life of its own, and cascaded like a ripple of fire to her shoulders.

'Did Mr. Treadmarsh have any suggestions to make?' Mrs. Stewart asked diffidently.

'Only that we're doing the right thing in selling up and moving to London.'

'I wish we'd done it a year ago. When I think how hard your father fought to stay on here....'

'It was a losing battle,' Amanda rejoined, determined not to let her mother wallow in sentiment. 'You can't fight the big boys; all you can do is join 'em.'

'You sound as if you're preparing to do so.'

'I am.' Amanda went to stand by the window, her eyes looking out on the garden but seeing instead the grey streets of London. 'I'm a better than average secretary and I know how to run a grocery shop. It's an unusual combination that should lead to an interesting job.'

'I think you should work in an office in the city. You're bound to meet a——'

'Nice young man,' Amanda finished. 'No, thanks, darling. I intend to do more with my future than look after a house and children for some bowler-hatted gent! I'm going to get myself a job with Brands. They're always advertising for staff.'

'You can't work for a supermarket!' Tears filled Mrs. Stewart's eyes. 'After the way Homefare treated your father, I'd have thought——'

'That's exactly why I want to work for Brands,' Amanda interrupted. 'They're Homefare's biggest rivals and if I can contribute in the smallest possible way to making them even bigger, I'll be delighted.'

Mrs. Stewart sighed. 'I wish you weren't so bitter. Forget the grocery business. You can't do anything to affect Homefare. It's like a whale, Amanda. It swallows up everything.'

'I might be able to give it indigestion!' Amanda said dryly. 'Stranger things have happened.'

With Amanda, to think was to act, and within a few weeks the lease of the shop had been disposed of at a giveaway price, the overdraft at the bank had been cleared and they were installed in a small flat in Camden Town. The rooms afforded a view of rooftops and grimy houses, but the rent was reasonable and the landlord a cheerful Indian with a plump wife and baby. It was far different from the quiet rooms of their village home, but when filled with their few antique pieces of furniture it at least looked habitable.

It was easier for Amanda to settle down than her mother, for within a week she had found herself a job at Brands, and was out of the flat for most of the day. It was only in the typing pool, but already she had worked two consecutive days for George Thomas, one of the food buyers for the group, who made it plain he would use her again when his own secretary was ill.

'It seems such a dull job for you,' her mother commented one evening a few months later when Amanda

10

returned home pale and tired after strap-hanging in the Tube. 'You had a good education and you're so lovely, I'm sure you could do something better.'

'You're biased, Mother,' Amanda smiled.

'No, I'm not. Mr. Chadwalla was very surprised when he heard you were a secretary. He was sure you were a model.'

'I'm a model secretary.'

'In a typing pool?'

'Not any more. I've been promoted.'

'That's marvellous. Why didn't you tell me?'

'You didn't give me a chance. It only happened this afternoon. Mr. Thomas's secretary is leaving and he's asked me to take her place. It's the first step up the ladder.' Amanda clasped her mother by the waist and danced her around the room. 'Wish me luck.'

Breathlessly Mrs. Stewart disengaged herself and sat down. 'Where's the luck in being a secretary?'

'I don't intend to remain one for long. I'm going to become a buyer myself.'

'Will it mean more money?'

'It isn't the money that's important. It means I'll be in direct competition with the Homefare buyer.'

'What good will that do? Really, Amanda, I wish you'd forget Homefare. You can't go on blaming them for your father's death. It was an accident.' Mrs. Stewart's voice was agitated and her lips had a bluish tinge that made Amanda regret she had allowed the conversation to continue.

Hurriedly she went into the bedroom and returned with a pill. 'Put it under your tongue,' she ordered, and watched as it was done.

Within a few moments the colour came back to Mrs. Stewart's lips and she gave an apologetic sigh. 'I'm

11

sorry, dear, I feel better now.'

'I'm the one who should be sorry. It was stupid of me to go on like that.'

Mrs. Stewart made no comment and Amanda changed the conversation, chatting about clothes and a dress she had seen on her way to work. But later that evening as she lay in bed and heard her mother's shallow breathing, she knew she could never eradicate the bitterness from her mind. As long as she lived she would remember her father's needless death and, remembering it, wish to pay back those who had caused it. How much easier it would be if it were a person and not a company. Sometimes she realised the futility of pitting herself against such a giant concern, but then she remembered David and Goliath and drew comfort from the thought. There must be thousands of small businesses which Homefare had destroyed on its way to becoming the mammoth organisation it now was. If only all the people whose livelihood it had taken away could band together into a rival group. It was an exciting thought but a hopeless one, and she forced it from her mind, knowing that unless she did so she would be unable to sleep. And sleep was important to a girl who was determined to show her new boss how capable she was.

Quickly Amanda settled into her new job, and within weeks had made herself indispensable to her employer.

'I don't know how I ever managed without you,' Mr. Thomas said one afternoon as she crossed the carpeted floor of his office to hand him his afternoon post to sign. 'I only gave you those letters an hour ago. You must have electric fingers, let alone an electric typewriter!' He glanced quickly through the pages, penning his signature at the bottom of each one as he did so. 'If you'd like to leave early, you may. I'm planning to leave early myself.'

'That *would* be nice,' Amanda smiled. 'Mrs. Grant said she'd take me to the Food Exhibition if I was free.'

'Still keen on becoming a buyer?'

'Yes.'

'You have no experience.'

'I helped my father. In the last six months I did all the ordering.'

'For a small shop? My dear Miss Stewart, one of our buyers spends as much in a day as you did in a year!'

'We were just as interested in getting the best possible products at the lowest price.'

'But do you have the knowledge to recognise the best products? You wouldn't be faced with a few products to choose from; you'd have dozens.'

Realising the futility of continuing the discussion, Amanda picked up the letters and retreated.

'About the dance on Saturday,' Mr. Thomas called as she reached the door. 'My wife and I would be delighted to have you sit at our table.'

'That's very kind of you,' Amanda lied. 'But I'm not sure if I'm coming.'

'You can't miss the Staff Dance.' Mr. Thomas was shocked. 'Everyone goes. You'll have the chance of seeing Mr. Brand too. He's a charming man. You must come, Miss Stewart, I've spoken so much about you to my wife that she's looking forward to meeting you.'

So that she can make sure I haven't got designs on her husband, Amanda thought, hiding a smile as she nodded and said that perhaps she would come to the dance after all.

'That's settled, then,' Mr. Thomas smiled. 'I'm sure you won't regret it. You'll be the belle of the ball.'

Mrs. Stewart seemed to think so too, though she was annoyed that Amanda had not bought herself a new dress.

'I've better things to do with my money,' Amanda told her.

'What could be better than buying yourself something pretty?'

'Giving you a holiday in the sun. It will do you good to get away from London.'

'I've no intention of taking a holiday,' Mrs. Stewart retorted. 'I feel fine.'

Unwilling to argue, Amanda turned away. She was perturbed at her mother's growing frailty and had made up her mind that a couple of months in the sunshine of Spain or Portugal would do more for her mother than the medicine and pills she received from her doctor.

'Amanda, you haven't heard one word I've said!'

'Sorry,' Amanda apologised. 'What was it?'

'Mrs. Chadwalla said she'd be delighted to lend you one of her saris. She has some beautiful ones.'

'I wouldn't even know how to put one on,' Amanda protested. 'And I'd look silly in it.'

'I think you'd look lovely. They're so graceful and feminine, and you've got just the right figure.'

With surprising speed Mrs. Stewart went to the door and, almost as if it had been prearranged, the landlady came in on a gust of curry, carrying a billowing cloud of blue and gold material over her arm. Within a moment it was draped around Amanda's slender form, deftly pleated at the waist and then tucked in, and draped across the bodice with one end of floating gossamer resting on her arm.

Amanda stared at herself with pleasure; by no stretch of the imagination did she look Indian, but her very air of modernity and bright red head emphasised the femininity of this most graceful of all traditional dress. Expecting the ponderous folds to hide her shape, she was astonished to see it emphasised it, drawing attention to her small waist and high, firm breasts. How long and slender her arms looked too, and how graceful the line of her neck and shoulders.

'If we draw your hair back so,' Mrs. Chadwalla hissed happily, pulling the thick red hair into a smooth coil on the nape of Amanda's neck, 'and then put on this little necklace'—a glittering affair of gilt and pearls cascaded around Amanda's throat—'you will look beautiful enough to be a Maharanee!'

'I feel like one,' Amanda giggled, and swung round, careful not to catch her heels in the skirt. 'But I couldn't wear this, Mrs. Chadwalla, it's yours.'

'It is yours,' the woman insisted. 'Two dozen like this lie in my wardrobe, and I wear none of them. Please be so good ... you will make me happy if you accept.'

Realising it would be churlish to refuse, Amanda nodded, and the next half hour was happily spent in learning how to put the sari on for herself.

'You will be the most beautiful girl at the dance,' the Indian woman said as she left to return to her own flat.

'I'll certainly be the most unusual-looking,' Amanda replied. 'The only red-headed Indian at the Dorchester!'

Three nights later Amanda bore out these words, and hovering by the ballroom door, wondered whether she wouldn't have been wiser to have worn her plain black silk. Several of the girls in the cloakroom had stared at her goggle-eyed as she had deposited her coat and disclosed her finery. But it was too late for regret, and clutching the floating end of her sari over her arm, she moved across to look at the table plans that had been set up at the entrance to the ballroom.

As Mr. Thomas had promised, she was sitting next to him and his wife, and she wended her way towards them, conscious of many male eyes following her progress.

Introductions made, she sat at the table, listening to Mrs. Thomas's superficial chatter and watching the colourful scene. Brands certainly spared no expense when it came to entertaining their staff; the large ballroom was packed with people, the majority of whom seemed to be dancing. Blue and white striped cloths—the Brands' colour scheme for their stores—covered beautifully laid tables whose assorted cutlery signified the elaborate meal to come.

'Would you care to dance with me?' Mr. Thomas asked. Amanda glanced quickly at his wife, who nodded her grey head encouragingly.

'I'm not one for dancing, myself,' she said cheerfully, 'but George likes to show what he can do on the floor.'

Mr. Thomas certainly did. Behind his desk he might be punctilious and ponderous, but on the dance floor he was a veritable Astaire, twirling Amanda around until she was breathless.

As though at a signal, people moved to the side of the floor, and Amanda saw with horror that they were

16

being left to perform on their own.

'This is the way I like floors to be,' said Mr. Thomas, deftly two-stepping as the band, seeing what was happening, played with even more enthusiasm. 'Never told you I was a ballroom champion, did I?'

'No,' said Amanda, and hoped her sari would not fall down around her feet. But apart from a few red-gold tendrils which clung damply to her forehead, she returned to the table unscathed, and was about to sit down when Mr. Thomas clutched her arm.

'Mr. Brand's coming over,' he whispered, and turned with a nervous smile to greet him.

Amanda had not given much thought to the man who had transformed Brands from a group of small shops to an important supermarket chain, but she was surprised by her first sight of Clive Brand, for he was completely different from her idea of a business tycoon. He was quiet and soft-spoken, with the restrained manner of an accountant rather than the self-made man she knew him to be. Grey hair at his temples and fine lines at the corners of his dark brown eyes showed him to be nearer forty than thirty, an impression confirmed by the small controlled mouth and smiling, but faintly aloof, expression. Here was a man who gave careful thought to every word he spoke; a far cry from the brash grocer image!

'I didn't know you were such an excellent dancer, Mr. Thomas.' Clive Brand's voice was as cultivated as his appearance, though it had an unexpected Canadian twang.

'I was lucky enough to find an excellent partner,' Mr. Thomas said with unexpected panache.

Dark brown eyes fixed themselves on Amanda and hastily Mr. Thomas made the introduction. Amanda felt her hand clasped in a cool firm one, and almost before she was aware of it, found herself on the dance floor again.

'I'm afraid I'm a more inhibited dancer,' Clive Brand apologised.

She smiled without comment, and for several moments they danced in silence. Close to him she realised he was slightly under average height, though he gave the appearance—because of his erect carriage—of being taller. He was certainly strong, for the arm around her waist was hard and sinewy, as were his shoulders beneath her hand. He seemed content to dance in silence, but glancing at him as the music stopped and he escorted her to her table, she saw he was watching her with an intensity she found unnerving.

'There is no Indian blood in you, Miss Stewart,' he said.

It took her a moment to realise what he meant, then she threw back her head and laughed. 'Only an Indian landlady! She gave me this sari as a present.'

'It suits you. It's an unusual outfit.'

'Does that mean *I'm* unusual?' she asked, and then stopped, remembering who he was.

'Beauty like yours is extremely unusual,' he replied.

Amanda was glad they had reached the table, for it saved her the embarrassment of replying. 'Thank you for the dance, Mr. Brand.'

'I must thank *you*.' He smiled fleetingly at the other occupants of the table and moved across to the next one.

He's obviously doing his duty dances, Amanda thought half-regretfully, as she settled herself down, but she had no more time for regret, for she was immediately asked on to the floor again. During the evening she caught the occasional glimpse of Clive Brand dancing with different women: the budding, ready-to-give-birth Mrs. Grant; hatchet-faced Mrs. Atkins who ran the accounts department, and the various regally gowned wives of his co-directors. Once his eyes met hers, but there was no recognition in them and, annoyed with herself for having expected it, she focused her attention on her partner, giving him such a beaming smile that he was emboldened to take advantage of it.

'You didn't come here with anyone, did you?' he asked and, as she shook her head, said: 'Then I hope you'll let me take you home.'

She gave a non-committal murmur, deciding that to accept Rodney Marsh's offer would result in unwanted gymnastics in the front seat of his car.

But he was not easy to elude, and when she went to the cloakroom to collect her coat later that evening, he went determinedly with her.

'We'll be happy to give you a lift, Miss Stewart,' Mr. Thomas said, catching sight of her as she re-emerged. 'Stay and talk to my wife while I see about a taxi.'

'I'm taking Amanda home,' Rodney Marsh said cheerily.

'I don't want to bother anyone,' Amanda interposed. 'It will be more convenient if I make my own way.'

'Don't be silly,' Rodney said, and put his arm around her shoulder. 'I'd love to take you home.'

'I don't doubt it,' she muttered, and tried to extricate herself from his hold.

'Don't be scared,' he grinned. 'I'm harmless.'

'I'm sure you are,' she lied, and again tried to

wriggle free.

'There you are, Miss Stewart,' a quiet voice said. 'I wondered whether you'd forgotten your promise to let me drive you home.'

Startled, she turned her head and saw Clive Brand. Rodney's arm fell away from her and with relief she stepped clear of him. 'Of course I haven't forgotten, Mr. Brand,' she said smoothly, and murmuring good-night to a stupefied Mr. and Mrs. Thomas and Rodney, she followed the head of Brands out of the carpeted foyer and into the back of a chauffeur-driven Rolls-Royce.

'You saved my life,' she said frankly.

'I was rather thinking of your virtue.'

The reply was so quietly made that it nearly passed her by, and her eyes narrowed as she looked at him in the gloom. He was sitting back in the corner, one well-tailored leg crossed over the other, his arms folded across his chest.

'How did you know I was having trouble with Rodney?' she asked artlessly.

'I was watching you for most of the evening.'

'I didn't notice.'

'I would have been annoyed with myself if you had.'

Again it was a remark that took digesting, and she chewed upon it carefully. There was more to this soft-spoken man than she had realised. Aware that he was her employer, she said carefully: 'It was kind of you to take me home. So many men think the offer of a lift is a licence for a free-for-all.'

'In my case, Miss Stewart, the warning is uncalled-for.'

She went scarlet. 'I didn't mean——'

'I think you did.' His small mouth curved in a smile.

'But I assure you I have no designs upon your honour.'

'Good,' she said in a little voice, and wished she could find a hole to bury herself in.

'I have other designs on you, though,' he continued, and as her startled gaze came up to his, added: 'Are you free to have dinner with me tomorrow? I'm sorry to make it such short notice, but I'm leaving for Montreal at the end of the week and I would like to see you before I go.'

'I'm free,' she said breathlessly, 'and I'd love to have dinner with you.'

'I'll call for you at eight, then. If it's a nice evening wear something casual and we'll have dinner in the country.'

He lapsed into silence, not speaking again until the Rolls stopped outside the terraced house in Camden Town and the chauffeur opened the car door for her.

'Until tomorrow, Miss Stewart,' he said, and waited till she had stepped into the small hallway before signalling his car to drive away.

CHAPTER TWO

AMANDA saw Clive Brand three times before he went to Canada. As arranged, he called for her the night after the Staff Dance—driving the Rolls himself—and took her to a quiet but expensive restaurant near Maidenhead where, at a table overlooking the river, she dined on the first of the season's grouse. Expecting to be in awe of him, she was surprised how easy it was to talk to him, though he himself talked little. Indeed, in order to find out about him she had been forced to ask Mr. Thomas, who informed her that Brands supermarkets spanned both sides of the Atlantic, being as well known in Canada as they were in England.

'Mr. Brand settled in London ten years ago,' he had concluded. 'I'm not sure why he made his home here. Maybe he prefers the life.'

This was one question Amanda felt she could ask Clive Brand without being considered inquisitive, and on her third evening with him she did so. 'Do you live in England from choice or because of business commitments?'

'From choice. I originally planned to stay here a couple of years—till I'd got Brands fully organised—but London grew on me. It has a quietness and detachment which I enjoy. People leave you alone here, if you want to be left alone.'

'Don't they in Canada?'

'Oh, sure, but I'm too well known over there ever to get real anonymity.'

Tentatively she considered the next question she wanted to ask, but decided against voicing it.

'I'm a widower,' he said, as if aware this had been the question in her mind. 'And back home I was the target for every match-making mother!'

'Doesn't that apply over here too?' Amanda smiled.

'Not with such insistence. Anyway, I pretend I've got a murky past. That at least keeps the fledglings off my back!'

She laughed outright at this. 'I can't imagine anyone thinking of you as a wolf.'

'I'm not a sheep, though.'

His tone was so dry that she looked at him from beneath her long, dark lashes, and decided that for all his quietness Mr. Brand was certainly no sheep. The three evenings she had spent with him had made her aware of his strength, not only physical but mental, for one only had to talk with him for a short time to recognise his determination to be a success.

'Your thoughts are now so deep that I can't read them any more,' he said.

'I'm glad. They were silly thoughts.'

'I'd still like to know them.' He reached across the table and caught her hand. 'Tell me, Amanda.'

Only rarely did he call her by her name and she had never yet called him by his, always resolutely waiting to catch his eye before speaking.

'I was wondering why you've been taking me out,' she said candidly. 'You've gone to great pains to let me know you're not a wolf, yet...'

'You're very beautiful and I like to be seen with beautiful women. It's good for my ego.'

'There are other girls more beautiful than I am,' she persisted, 'and well-known ones too.'

'I don't need to escort the famous. I have reached a stage in my life when I only go out with someone because I want to do so.' His fingers tightened around hers. 'And I want to be with you very much. I wanted it from the moment I saw you. You were the most striking-looking girl at the Dorchester that night.'

'The only one in a sari,' she said lightly, and wondered why she should be embarrassed by the compliment. It wasn't as though she was unused to them, so perhaps it was the man himself who was affecting her; she had never before met anyone like him.

'The sari made me notice you more quickly,' he agreed, 'but you are so beautiful I would have noticed you anyway. You should play up to your colouring, Amanda; wear things to complement your glorious hair.'

'I used to hate it when I was a child,' she confessed. 'Even now I get murderous if anyone calls me carrot-top.'

'I think the colour's more like a pomegranate. It has a soft, pinky gold look that I've never seen before.'

'What a lovely compliment!'

'I'm stating a fact.' He drew his hand away to signal for the bill, and soon they were speeding back towards London. 'I would like to show you my house,' he said suddenly. 'Unless you have any objection to coming home with me?'

'Should I have?'

'Remembering your reluctance to go home the other night with that young man with freckles....'

'You're not like Rodney,' she assured him.

'Thanks!' He glanced at her. 'I suppose I must seem old to you?'

'I hadn't thought about it,' she lied.

'Think about it now.'

Embarrassed, she did so, knowing he had not made the request lightly but was waiting for her reply.

'You're older than most of the men I've been out with,' she said slowly, 'and of course you're my boss. That makes a difference to the way I see.'

He stopped the car with such abruptness that the seatbelt almost flattened her. 'Don't ever say that to me again! You may work for my company, but I'm not your boss.'

Astonished at his unexpected reaction, she stared at him, and, aware of it, he seemed to realise an explanation was necessary. 'I met my wife when she was working for me, and whenever we had a row she used to say she only married me because I was her boss. As you can imagine, it rather soured me on the idea.'

'I'm not surprised.'

He sighed. 'We were not very happy. We separated five years ago and she died a year later.'

'Is that why you came to England?'

'Subconsciously perhaps, though I've always wanted to live here. The ambience of London suits me.'

He set the car in motion again and they drove the rest of the way in companionable silence. It was ten o'clock when they reached the tall, Regency house in a small square off Hyde Park, and entering it and moving from one lovely room to another, all furnished with priceless antiques, Amanda began to appreciate what his particular ambience was.

'Have you always been interested in the past?' she asked, her eyes ranging from the hand-tooled first editions on the library shelves to the Constables and Fantin Latours on the walls.

'Ever since I could afford it.' He looked at her gravely. 'My father was a farmer, you know. He ground out a living in the prairie and until she was fifty the nearest my mother ever came to a house like this was a four-roomed shack.' He paused and then said: 'She died owning one of the most magnificent homes in Montreal.'

'Is that why you set so much store by possessions?' She bit her lip. 'Forgive me, that sounded awfully rude.'

'Don't apologise, Amanda. I like your curiosity. It at least shows you're interested in me!' He went over to a Queen Anne bureau on which stood a silver tray with a bottle of champagne reposing in an ice-bucket. 'Would you care for a drink?'

'You're spoiling me,' she smiled as she accepted a

glass from him. 'I thought champagne was only for celebrations.'

'This *is* a celebration.'

'For what?'

'My first real evening with you.'

'Didn't our other two evenings count?'

'Not in the same way. You see, tonight, I made up my mind that——' He looked into his glass and Amanda waited, afraid without knowing why. 'I'll telephone you when I return from Canada,' he said, as though he had been talking about his trip. 'I hope to be back next Thursday, so keep the evening free. If I'm delayed, my secretary will let you know.'

To her surprise Amanda found she was looking forward to seeing Clive Brand again, though she was honest enough to acknowledge that this might be due to who he was, rather than what he was. After all, it was difficult not to consider it a feather in her cap to have captured the attention of the man who was king of the small world in which she worked.

She half expected him to telephone her from Canada; these days it was a matter of moments to make a transatlantic call, but he did not do so, and even on the following Thursday—when she was supposed to be seeing him—there was no word to let her know whether or not he had returned to England. Yet he had promised that his secretary would call her if he was delayed and, remembering this, she changed into one of her prettiest dresses when she came home from the office.

'Are you seeing Mr. Brand again?' her mother asked.

'I'm not sure.'

'Do you think it's wise? You work for him and——'

'He nearly blew his top when *I* said that,' Amanda smiled.

'It's the truth, and it can make things awkward for you if you don't want to see him again.'

'I can't imagine Clive feeling awkward about anything I did,' Amanda said candidly. 'He's the most self-contained man I've ever met.'

'Opposite from you, then. You're so transparent with your emotions you're like a book without a cover!'

'What a devastating thing to say! I must remember to hide my feelings. It isn't good to let a man know you like him.'

'Do you like Mr. Brand?' Mrs. Stewart asked.

'Very much. He's so stable and steady. Not a bit the way I imagined a supermarket tycoon to be.'

'That's because you keep thinking of the Homefare people.'

Amanda tossed her head, but before she could reply a hooter sounded in the street and, looking through the window she saw the Rolls. With a breathless good-bye to her mother she ran downstairs.

Sitting next to Clive, it was difficult to believe she had not seen him for a week, for his greeting was as calm as though they had only parted the night before. Yet watching him surreptitiously as he drove through the crowded streets to the West End, she thought he looked more tired than usual, and that the grey at his temples was more noticeable. It was hard enough to control a vast business complex in England, let alone one which spanned both sides of the Atlantic. Hadn't she read somewhere that jet travel was ageing, or did that only apply to travel in space?

'Why are you smiling?' he asked.

Unaware that she had been, she shook her head. 'It wasn't important.'

'Everything you think is important. Tell me.'

Sheepishly she did so, and felt even more foolish when he chuckled. 'It's exactly the opposite with space travel, my dear. The faster you go, the less you age in earth terms. It's part of Einstein's theory of relativity that if a man travels in space for a considerable time— say a journey of a hundred and fifty years—when he returned to earth he would find that several generations had been born and died in his absence.' The dark eyes regarded her intently before focusing on the traffic again. 'I'm sorry if my week's absence made you afraid I would turn into Rip Van Winkle.'

She went scarlet. 'I only thought you looked tired.'

'I don't feel at my best,' he admitted, 'but one never does after six hours in a plane and a time-change.'

'It would have been better if you hadn't seen me tonight.'

'I wanted to see you. I missed you.'

The car stopped and she saw they were at the Mirabelle. Leaving it to be parked by the doorman, he escorted her downstairs. He shook his head when asked if they wanted to have a drink at the bar, and indicated that he wished to go immediately to his table.

Sitting at a white-decked one in the corner of the large, well-lit room, Amanda looked with curiosity at the well-dressed people around her, and was glad she had chosen to wear black. Her dress was inexpensive and plain, but its very simplicity made it difficult to assess its price, and its clear, uncluttered lines revealed the lovely ones of her figure.

'Don't waste your time looking at the other women here,' Clive whispered. 'You're the most beautiful one

28

in the room.'

'Now I really know you're back,' she smiled. 'No one ever pays me such compliments.'

'I hope you don't give any other man the chance.'

'You can't expect me to live like a nun.'

'Socially no, but physically yes.' He paused. 'Are you?'

Her head tilted sharply, annoyance overcoming her embarrassment. 'I am, as a matter of fact.'

'Good.'

'I didn't know you were so old-fashioned, Clive.' She said his name for the first time, surprised to find it came out so easily.

'I don't like owning second-hand goods.'

'I'm not one of your goods,' she retorted.

'My dear, I'm sorry. That was a clumsy way to put it. I meant it as a compliment, not an insult.'

Though mollified she was still irritated, and throughout the evening found herself thinking of what he had said. He did regard her as a possession of his, despite his denial. The way he harped on her beauty and his pleasure at being seen with her signified this. He would not take her out if she were fat and ugly. But then what man would? Chiding herself for being foolish, she concentrated on what he was saying.

'And so,' he concluded, 'it would be better for both of us if you didn't work for Brands any more.'

Astonished, she stared at him. 'Are you firing me?' She saw his expression and said hastily, 'I'm sorry, Clive, but I missed the beginning of what you said.'

'Obviously.' He leaned across the table. 'I was suggesting that you left Brands. I'm in love with you, Amanda, and I want to marry you. When our engagement is announced it would be better if you were not one of my employees.'

Amanda swallowed hard, unable to credit that she was hearing correctly. 'Are you proposing to me?'

'Why do you sound so surprised? Didn't you know I would?'

'Of course I didn't!' Indignation made her voice rise, and aware that several people were looking at them, she reddened. 'Really, Clive, what a way to ask a girl to marry you—by telling her she's fired! A proposal like that should go into the Guinness Book of Records!'

His smile was slight and fleeting. 'I was hoping you'd understand why I said it, without my having to explain.'

'It isn't the explanation that's bothering me,' she said crossly. 'It's the way you've proposed. I mean, how do you know I love you?'

'I don't.' His face was impassive. 'But *I* love you and I'll do everything in my power to make *you* love *me*.'

'How *can* you love me? You hardly know me.'

'Let's call it instinct. Or intuition if you prefer it. When I look for a site for a new supermarket I take my car and drive around the town where I wish to build it. Suddenly I'll stop in a particular street. There won't be any logical reason for me to stop there—only a feeling that tells me that this particular spot is the right one.'

'And I'm a particular spot, am I?' Amanda asked.

'Very particular,' he said quietly, 'and very special. Now stop looking so beautifully indignant and concentrate on the menu. You'll feel less like devouring me once you've devoured some food!'

His unexpected humour, for he was not normally a

funny man, lessened her indignation at such a blunt proposal, and made her able to see it from his point of view. He was a millionaire who had fallen in love with a working girl, and logically he could be forgiven for assuring that the girl would fall into his lap like a ripe plum.

'I'm no plum,' she said aloud. 'I won't marry you just because you're rich.'

'I'm delighted to hear it,' he said gravely, following her train of thought with commendable agility. 'Now order something to eat and we'll talk later.'

Deliberately she chose the most expensive meal she could: caviar, lobster and an extravagant concoction of chestnut, whipped cream and meringue. Only as they reached the coffee stage did she realise that Clive had been right. Replete, she no longer felt angry and could view his proposal with a calmness she had not felt earlier.

'I'm glad you've recovered your equilibrium,' he said, and leaning back in his chair studied her without pretending that he was not doing so.

'Do I suit you?' she asked lightly.

'Very much. That's why I want you to be my wife.'

'Only because I'm beautiful?'

'I would never have been attracted to you if you'd been ugly. Would you have gone out with *me* if I'd been a three-foot dwarf?'

'Only if *I'd* been two-foot-one!' She couldn't help laughing. 'You're so logical, Clive, it's difficult to argue with you.'

'That augurs well for our future together.'

'I haven't yet said I'll marry you.' She looked at him with the candour he was bestowing on her. It was wrong for there to be any pretence between them. Indeed she owed him the truth, for when it came to a question of their happiness it would be foolish to lie. 'I'm not sure how I feel about you, Clive. I like you very much, I may even be in love with you, but I'm not sure. If you weren't who you are—so important, I mean, and rich—it would be easier for me to know if what I feel for is the real thing or just the excitement of being wanted by a millionaire.'

'I'm richer than that, Amanda.'

Her mouth fell open, then she threw back her head and laughed, a warm vibrant sound as uninhibited as she herself usually was. 'Honestly, Clive, do you take everything so literally?'

'I'm afraid I do.' He was rueful. 'It's part of the reason for my success in business, and probably the main reason why my marriage was a failure.'

'What went wrong?' she asked, and then said quickly: 'I'm sorry, I had no right to ask.'

'You have every right.' His small mouth pursed forward, the lower lip full and pensive. 'I don't think Anne ever loved me. It was as simple as that. She married me because of my position.'

'Why did you marry *her*?'

'Because she was beautiful.' His eyes narrowed as he saw Amanda's expression. 'I worship beauty,' he went on. 'There's no point in my denying it.'

'A wife is more than just a beautiful object,' Amanda said bluntly. 'And beautiful women can sometimes become plainer wives!'

'You could never be plain, my darling.'

'Not even if I were pregnant and fat?'

He frowned. 'I hadn't thought of you with children. I want to be your entire life, Amanda.' He reached for her hand. 'But if you want a child, I'll be happy

32

to oblige.'

She laughed and blushed. 'Not till I accept your proposal!'

'Does that mean you——'

'I don't know yet,' she interrupted. 'Give me time to think about it. If I married you, it wouldn't be because of your bank balance, but because you're the man I want to spend the rest of my life with. My parents were idyllically happy, and I like to think I can be the same.'

'When can I meet your parents?'

'My father is dead.'

'I'm sorry, I had no idea. You've never spoken of them.'

'We haven't had much opportunity.'

'Tell me about them now,' he said, and listened quietly as she did so.

Once she began she found it a relief to unburden herself, and she made no attempt to hide her bitterness at what she believed to be the cause of her father's accident and death.

'I can understand how you feel,' Clive said as she finished, 'but as a supermarket owner myself I see it from Homefare's point of view. Not that I have much sympathy for them,' he went on. 'Charles Foster is not a man I care for. He's too arrogant.'

'Charles Foster?' she questioned.

'The owner of Homefare.'

'I thought it was a public company.'

'It is, but Foster owns the majority of the shares, and he's a law unto himself.'

'A law you don't agree with?' she asked with interest.

'A law I frequently clash with.' Clive's lips clamped

together, giving his jaw a more determined thrust. 'It wouldn't be exaggerating if I said I thoroughly detest him.'

Amanda's curiosity was aroused. Clive had never before spoken with such vehemence about anyone or anything, and since this antipathy was directed against someone whom she herself loathed, she longed to know more.

'Why don't you like him?'

'Because he's got an uncanny ability to get his hands on sites that I want. He's already pipped me to the post seven times this year.'

'So many?' she said in surprise, and saw him look at her tenderly.

'I have a hundred and forty-two supermarkets, my darling, and Homefare has a hundred and fifty.'

'I can't think of you as being so important.'

'Good. I only want you to think of me as the man who loves you and wants to be your husband. I'll take care of you when you leave Brands, and when we're married——'

'You'll do nothing of the sort,' she protested. 'I've no intention of letting you keep me.'

He pushed back his chair. 'Let's talk about it in the car.'

But once in the car he did not refer to the subject, and drove in silence along Park Lane and into Hyde Park. Carefully he found a secluded spot bordering the Serpentine, then stopped the car by the water's edge and turned off the engine.

'Now what's all this nonsense about refusing to let me look after you financially?' he demanded. 'As I'm asking you to leave Brands—and I'm sure you understand the reason why——'

'Of course I understand the reason. But that doesn't mean you need to keep me. I'll get another job. If I don't marry you I'll have to get another job anyway.'

'I wish you didn't need time to make up your mind,' he burst out. 'I'm so sure of my feelings that I hoped you'd feel the same about me.'

'I'm almost sure,' she whispered, touched by the hurt in his voice, 'but I have to be positive.'

'Will this help?' He drew her close and pressed his face against hers. It was the first time he had held her since the night they had danced together, but here, in the confines of his car, it had a greater intimacy and she responded to it. Putting her arms around his neck, she pressed closer to him. She was aware of his fine silky hair beneath her fingers and the smooth skin of his cheek as he rubbed it against her own.

'It feels like velvet,' he murmured, 'and it looks like it too ... creamy velvet.'

His lips rested on hers. They were soft and slightly moist and she was aware of their anxious movement and the sudden trembling of his body.

'I want you so much,' he whispered against her mouth. 'Don't make me wait too long.'

Nervously she drew away from him, and he sat for a long moment hunched over the wheel as though he lacked the energy to do anything else. It reminded her that he had had a long flight from Canada and she felt an upsurge of tenderness for him.

'It's late, Clive. You should be in bed.'

'I wish I was—with you.' He switched on the ignition. 'Don't be scared, my dear. I'll take you safely home!'

It was only as he stopped the car in front of the terraced house in Camden Town that he made any mention of their next meeting.

'I have a sales conference with my managers tomorrow and I'm not sure what time I'll be free in the evening. It will be better if we leave it until Saturday.'

'You don't need to see me every night,' she smiled.

'I need it very much,' he said without smiling back. 'I won't be happy until you belong to me.'

The words remained with her long after he had gone, once more arousing a faint disquiet which she could not totally dispel. It was silly to be worried by the remark. It proved her mother was right when she said she should start to think of marriage. Having to make one's own way in life could lead to an independence of spirit that could make her rebel against the give and take of marriage.

Yet for Clive to use the word 'belong' did not augur well for their future. It smacked of proprietorship, of a belief that the wife was a chattel and not a partner. But was it a partner that he was looking for, or was it a beautiful girl whom he could put on a pedestal for other people to admire?

It was a question she could not answer, and until she was able to do so she knew she could not agree to marry him. She liked him and she was happy when she was with him, but whether or not this feeling would lead to something deeper was something that only time would tell.

CHAPTER THREE

WHEN Amanda took out her pay cheque from the buff-coloured envelope next morning, there was a pink slip inside terminating her employment and giving her a month's salary in lieu of notice. Clive certainly worked fast! Half amused, half annoyed, she wondered if Mr. Thomas knew she had been dismissed, and was considering how to explain it to him when he called her into his office and broached the matter himself.

'Mr. Brand has told me of his expectations,' he said primly, 'and naturally I am delighted for you. Delighted. My only regret is that I have to lose a perfect secretary.'

'I'm sorry I have to leave so suddenly,' Amanda apologised. 'I had intended to give you a month's notice, but,' she tapped the envelope she was holding, 'this makes it impossible. Mr. Brand wants me to leave today.'

'I'm sure you can appreciate why. When your friendship with him becomes common knowledge there will be a lot of publicity.'

'It's nothing *more* than friendship so far,' Amanda protested.

Mr. Thomas looked as if he could not believe that any girl needed to consider whether or not to accept Clive Brand's proposal.

'Mr. Brand is a charming and intelligent man. Any girl lucky enough to get the chance of ... Still, it's your life, Miss Stewart. Whatever you decide, I wish you happiness.'

'Thank you.' She came closer to the desk. 'Until I

do make a decision, I'll have to find another job. I can't sit at home waiting while I ... I can't sit at home,' she reiterated.

'Don't worry about your reference. I'll give you an excellent one,' Mr. Thomas said at once. 'I'm sure you won't have any trouble finding other employment.' Then, playfully wagging his finger at her: 'But don't go to our rivals, will you? Mr. Brand wouldn't like that.'

'Why should I go *there*?'

'They've taken half-page advertisements in most of the national papers this morning. Vacancies for staff. It's just the extravagant sort of thing they do.'

'It doesn't seem to affect their profits,' she replied. 'They've just announced higher dividends!'

'Considering their cut-throat methods of business, I'm not surprised.'

The entry of Mr. Thomas's assistant prevented Amanda from replying, and she returned to her desk.

At mid-morning there was a lull in telephone calls, and she picked up the morning paper and glanced at the advertisement which had so offended Mr. Thomas. Like all Homefare adverts it was bright and to the point, leaving the reader in no doubt as to what was being said. This time they were not promoting cut-price offers of food but high-salaried staff vacancies. An image of Charles Foster hovered in her mind. Clive had said they were totally dissimilar, and she had a picture of a loud-voiced barrow boy; but a highly intelligent barrow boy nonetheless, for it had taken more than energy to create a supermarket chain like Homefare. Certainly its brash methods was one of the reasons why Clive was so disapproving. He liked to do things in a conservative fashion with nothing left to chance, the way he was trying to organise her own life. The thought came into her mind too quickly to be monitored, and she was annoyed with herself for thinking it. Yet it was true. Because he wished to make her his wife and had been certain she would eventually accept him, he had fired her so as to avoid any gossip that she might be marrying him for his money and prestige. Yet in sending her away he had not taken into account the possibility that she might turn down his proposal and, in doing so, be faced with the problem of finding other employment.

His offer to take care of her until she had made up her mind did not even bear thinking of. It would serve him right if she got a job at Homefare. The thought made her grin, though her amusement faded as she remembered the way her father had died. If only she could stop thinking of it with such deep bitterness! She still blamed Homefare for it, despite knowing it was wrong of her to do so. Working at Brands had given her sufficient knowledge of the grocery world to know that small shops would inevitably fall by the wayside; for her father to have fought against the tide had been unrealistic.

Mother's right, Amanda thought. No one person can be responsible for changing customs; it occurs spontaneously and can never be held back. Perhaps if I worked for Homefare and learned how *they* ticked. I wouldn't feel bitter at all.

Without giving herself time to reconsider, she dialled the number given in the advertisement and made an appointment to see the staff supervisor during the lunch hour.

At one o'clock, armed with an excellent reference, she presented herself at the head office of Homefare.

Like Brands it occupied its own building, but unlike Brands it was a hive of bustle and noise. Even the people seemed different; not afraid to talk loudly as they walked through the corridors and popping in and out of various offices with loud greetings.

But personnel officers were the same the world over, and Amanda was bombarded with questions before being escorted two flights up to a large corner office filled with samples of food merchandise. In the centre of the room, surveying it all with a calm air, was a plump and cheerful man with a ruddy complexion and grey hair.

Ten minutes later Amanda had been offered and had accepted the job of private secretary to Gordon Craig, at a salary far higher than she was already receiving. Only when she re-entered the austere precincts of Brands did she feel a qualm at what she had done, and wondered how angry Clive would be. It was strange to think of him as Clive. When she had come to work here she had never dreamt she would be leaving because of her friendship with the man to whom all this belonged. It was an overwhelming thought and she wondered if she was stupid not to have agreed to marry him at once. What a difference it would make to her life if she did! No more small flat and noisy neighbours; no more worrying about her mother's health and whether or not she could afford to send her away during the English winter. Married to Clive she would know undreamed-of luxury. She tried to envisage herself the mistress of his home, but though her imagination took her into the house, it could not take her into his bedroom. The intimacy of being his wife had an unreality that refused to grow clearer. She frowned, not sure why this was so. She was no prude and looked forward to the physical relationship she would share with the man she loved. But perhaps she did not love Clive enough. It was this uncertainty which had made her plead for more time.

Amanda's imminent departure from Brands was common knowledge before the end of the day, and several of the secretaries came in to say goodbye, automatically assuming she was leaving because she had been offered more money.

'Let me know if you meet old Foster,' one of the girls said. 'He's supposed to be a real dragon.'

'If I see any smoke in the corridor I'll run a mile!' Amanda grinned.

'I've heard he's a recluse,' someone else chipped in, and two more added equally exaggerated reports as to his appearance and behaviour, each one more horrendous than the last.

Amanda refused to let it dissuade her from taking up her position with Gordon Craig, but she eventually found herself repeating some of the remarks to him after she had been his secretary for a fortnight. It had been two weeks of surprise, not the least of which had been the easy-going manner between all the employees who, nonetheless, referred to each other by their surnames.

'It's one of Mr. Foster's idiosyncrasies,' Gordon Craig had explained on Amanda's first day. 'We call some of the juniors by their first names, but in general everyone else is called either Miss or Mrs. Mr. Foster believes that if the senior executives demand respect, they should also return the courtesy.'

Amanda had made no comment at the time, but now she felt sufficiently at home to do so. 'I didn't think Mr. Foster cared much about politeness. I've heard

41

he's a rough diamond.'

'If gossip is running true to form, I bet you've heard more than that,' Mr. Craig smiled.

'Well, he is rather a mystery man, isn't he?'

'He keeps to himself, if that's what you mean. But he knows everything that goes on.'

'Some of the staff think the offices are bugged,' Amanda said before she could stop herself.

Mr. Craig choked on the cup of coffee he was sipping and took a moment to recover. 'Mr. Foster's knowledge of his staff isn't derived from electronic assistance! It comes from his understanding of people.'

'I suppose it *is* important to understand people if you want to get the better of them.'

The look on Mr. Craig's face told her she had said too much, and hurriedly gathering up the letters he had signed, she went to the door. But she was not to escape so easily, for as she reached it, he called her back.

'Do I detect a note of censure in your last remark, Miss Stewart?'

'Aren't I allowed to criticise the great Mr. Foster?'

'You may say what you like,' came the impatient reply. 'I merely thought you were too intelligent to criticise someone you didn't know.'

'I know quite a lot about Mr. Foster.'

'Indeed?'

'My father owned a grocery shop which Homefare wanted to buy. It was in a small village near Brigford. He wouldn't sell, and when you opened your supermarket in the town, he was forced out of business.'

'Those sort of things happen.' Gordon Craig spoke impersonally. 'I hope your father found other employment?'

'He died,' she said, and this time was not called

back as she went to the door.

Returning to her office after lunch, she found a booklet on her desk. It was a history of Homefare Supermarkets; from its small beginning as a one-roomed store in a market town to its present-day position as one of the largest groups in the country. Though it had made several take-overs during the past decade, its main success had come from building larger and larger stores, for it had been one of the first companies to appreciate the value of selling articles for the home as well as food for the kitchen. Despite other groups following close on their heels, Homefare still managed to keep a step ahead of all its competitors. They were one of the first chains to provide massive parking space for their customers, and were now concentrating on hypermarkets: vast warehouses where everything for one's home could be obtained at discount prices. As an exercise in propaganda the book was excellent, and to complete the picture a full description of all the directors was given. Only the name Charles Foster appeared without any additional information, save that he was managing director and grandson of the founder. It was as good a reason as any for being in charge, Amanda decided cynically; even without any ability the position would have been his. But could he have achieved it on his own merits if, like Clive, he had been brought up in a three-roomed shack?

Warmed by an appreciation of Clive's ability, Amanda greeted him with greater affection when he called for her that evening, hooting on the Rolls to let her know that he had arrived, and keeping the engine running so that he could drive off the moment she entered the car.

'I thought we'd dine at my home tonight,' he told

her. 'I want to alter the furnishings in the dining-room and I'd like your opinion.'

'I doubt if you would,' Amanda laughed. 'I like bright colours.'

'I must say I prefer muted ones,' he admitted, 'but if you want something more positive we'll go ahead and have it.'

'Oh no, it's *your* dining-room.'

'I'm hoping it will be yours too. I love you and I want you to be happy in my home—our home. How much longer are you going to take to make up your mind?'

'It's only a fortnight since you asked me,' she protested.

'I'm lonely.'

'But you're so busy.'

'All the more reason why I need a hostess.'

The answer chilled her and she tried to reason it away. Of course Clive needed a hostess. It was silly to have expected him to say he needed her as a woman, that he wanted to hold her and love her. He obviously wanted that too, but was not the sort of man who would find it easy to say so.

'What are you thinking about, darling?' he asked.

'You,' she said candidly. 'Whether I'm the right girl to make you happy. I'm not sure I can give you what you need.'

'I'm not asking you to give me anything. Just being with you is all I want; to know I can look up and see you in front of me; that when I'm away from you I can picture you in my home.'

It was the most romantic declaration he had yet made and she slid across the seat and snuggled next to him. She was still by his side when they reached his house, and hand in hand they went in to dinner.

As she had expected, the food was good without being ostentatious. Melon, roast lamb and vegetables and fresh fruit; but the china and cutlery were exquisite and the service of the butler faultless. Only when they reached the coffee stage and were alone, did Clive ask for her suggestions on redecoration, but for some reason she was still loath to give them, and sensing her reluctance he let the matter drop and turned the conversation to her new job.

'I have the impression you went to Homefare deliberately.'

She widened her blue eyes at him. 'Really?'

'Really,' he mocked. 'Come now, be honest and admit it.'

'I thought it would serve you right,' she confessed. 'I suppose I was annoyed with you for firing me.'

'I told you why I did it, and I also said I wanted to take care of you.'

'Let's not go into that,' she pleaded.

'Very well.'

He pushed back her chair and ushered her into the drawing-room. It was formal and austere, despite the profusion of flowers, and looking around her she could understand why Clive wanted a wife. Few housekeepers, however competent, had the ability to make a house into a home. Yet how could she alter things if she lived here? Scatter books and magazines around? Change the stiff curtains for softer ones? Or did the rooms only need to be lived in and loved in to take on warmth? It was an interesting thought, but one she did not have time to consider, for Clive was talking to her again, and had been talking for several minutes, she realised guiltily. She forced herself to concentrate

45

on what he was saying, managing by quick thinking to catch up on what she had missed. It was a diatribe against Charles Foster, who seemed to possess the ability of buying plum spots in new development centres before anyone else had heard of them.

'How he managed to get hold of the Hanlow site is beyond me,' Clive concluded. 'My own men were on to it months ago, yet he beat us to it.'

'Perhaps he offered more money?'

'If it were only that I'd know how to fight it.' He put up a hand, a well-shaped one, with the nails shiny as though they were manicured, and rubbed the side of his face. 'It's more than money, Amanda.'

He pulled his lip. 'I'd give anything if I could prove connivance. I'm sure that's the only thing that helped him to get the Hanlow site.'

'Is it a good one?'

'The best,' he said shortly. 'A growing town with a rising lower middle-class population. I was sure the site was mine.'

He moved restlessly around the room. She had not see him so agitated before and it somehow made him more human.

'I'll ask Mr. Craig about it,' she ventured. 'He seems to know Mr. Foster very well.'

'He's hardly likely to admit they used influence to get the site.'

'He might mention something of interest if I can get him to talk about it.'

'It's kind of you to offer,' Clive said stiffly. 'But recounting gossip won't help me.'

'Then I won't ask him anything.' Amanda crossed her hands in her lap and sat up straight like a little girl who has been reprimanded.

With unusual awareness of her mood Clive came over and knelt at her side. 'Don't be angry with me, dearest. It's sweet of you to be so concerned.'

She melted at his kind words, her blue eyes darkening. 'I wish I could help you.'

His arms came around her, drawing her close. 'You might, at that. Just let me know if they're looking for other sites and in what areas.'

Amanda pulled back from him. 'Are you asking me to spy for you?'

'Would you be angry if I were?'

She frowned and then, giving it more thought, shook her head. 'Not really. I mean, people in business do that sort of thing, don't they? I'm only surprised you should ask *me* to do it for you.'

'Who better to ask than the person you love and trust?'

It was a novel comeback and she could not help smiling. Seeing it, Clive smiled back at her.

'Forget it, darling.' He stood up and walked over to the sideboard. 'Would you care for a brandy?'

She shook her head and watched as he poured one for himself, and returned with it to sit in the chair opposite. 'Why is it important for you to know where Homefare is expanding?' she asked. 'I'd have thought the country was big enough for both of you.'

'Some positions can't be bettered. In the past few years those are the ones Charles Foster has managed to get.' Clive sipped his brandy. 'Right now we're both competing for hypermarket sites. They require far more land and consequently they're harder to find. If I knew where he was looking—the places he has in mind—I might be able to step in ahead of him.'

Mention of the word 'hypermarket' reminded her

of her father, and any qualms she might have had about passing on information to Clive were dissolved by the bitterness of her memories. 'If I can find out anything, I'll let you know,' she told him.

'Thank you for saying that.' He put down his glass and drew her up from the chair and on to his lap. 'My beautiful Amanda,' he said gravely, and pressed his lips to her throat.

For a long while they remained close and Clive displayed a passion he had so far held in check, though at her first exclamation he let her go and apologised.

'You make it so easy for me to lose my control,' he said contritely. 'Forgive me.'

She smiled and waited for him to take her in his arms again and override her fears, but instead he picked up his brandy and sipped it. Watching the pink flush slowly leave his face she sensed he did not like to be put at a disadvantage, nor did he wish to overcome her with his own desire. Yet if he wanted her enough, surely he would try to do so? Most men would, she knew, but then Clive wasn't like most men. There was a reserve about him which she found disquieting.

She jumped to her feet. 'It's late. I must go.'

'Please make up your mind about me soon, Amanda. I need you.' His lids lowered, masking his eyes. 'I'm sorry, I always seem to be saying that.'

'Don't apologise for it,' she said quickly. 'That's something no woman gets tired of hearing.'

CHAPTER FOUR

AMANDA thought no more of her promise to Clive to find out where Homefare were hoping to open new hypermarkets, until she went into Mr. Craig's office late one afternoon of the following week and heard him talking on the telephone. From the tone of his voice she knew it was to someone important, but it was not until she heard him say Mr. Foster that she realised it was the Chairman.

Quietly she put her letters on the desk and then, as she usually did, sat down to wait until they were signed. Normally she would not have listened to the telephone conversation, but with Clive's request vivid in her mind, she did so, her senses on the alert as Mr. Craig began to talk about a new site.

'It would be first rate for a hypermarket and not all that expensive to develop. I've already worked out some of the costings.' He made a note on his pad, then spoke again. 'Yes, I have that. Six-thirty, you say? Very well, Mr. Foster, that will be fine.' The receiver was set in its cradle and mild grey eyes stared at Amanda. 'Now for the letters,' he said, and began to sign them. 'When you've prepared these for the post you can go.' He handed the folder across to her and she took it but did not move.

'Are Homefare going to open another hypermarket?' she asked artlessly.

'As many as we can,' he smiled. 'Mr. Foster has big plans for the company.'

'I don't suppose any of the other directors dare to disagree with him.'

49

'On the contrary, Miss Stewart; though in this case they happen to agree with him completely.'

Sensing the rebuke, she flushed. 'I'm sorry, Mr. Craig, I just had the impression that Mr. Foster likes to get his own way.'

'He does. But that doesn't mean he forces his point of view on to the other members of the Board. Not that he couldn't do so if he wished. He's the majority shareholder.'

'Why does he work so hard if he's so rich?'

'He loves the cut and thrust of business.'

'More cut than thrust,' she said before she could stop herself.

'You do seem to have been listening to gossip! I take it you are repeating what you heard at Brands?'

The accusation was so true she could not deny it.

'You can understand why,' she said stiffly. 'The two companies are rivals.'

'All to the good. There's nothing like competition for keeping prices down.' He pointed to the folder. 'Don't miss the post with those, my dear.'

With a murmur of apology for keeping him talking, she went out, and was still pretending to be busy at her desk when he came through her office to say good-night, and left.

Guiltily she found herself things to do, hoping that the thudding of her heart would not be heard by anyone except herself. Soon the entire building was deserted, and peering through the window she saw that the car park far below was empty save for one solitary vehicle. Hurriedly she went into Mr. Craig's office and glanced at the papers on his desk. There were none she did not recognise, and feeling like a thief, she pulled his pad towards her. He had jotted down several notes during his conversation with Mr. Foster and it might be possible to decipher them. But the pad was unmarked, and partly disappointed, partly relieved, she put it down. If she were unable to find anything Clive could not accuse her of not wanting to help him, whereas if she found something and did not tell him, she would feel disloyal. Yet surely it was better to feel disloyal towards Homefare than to Clive? She tossed her head. What loyalty did she owe a company who was responsible for the last six, unhappy months of her father's life? Hardened by the thought, she picked up the pad again and peered at it. Mr. Craig had torn off the sheet on which he had been writing, but faint indentations had come through on to this one. Tearing it off the pad, she lifted it towards the light. As she did so, she saw a dark shadow through the glass door.

'Who is it?' she called sharply.

'I was about to ask the same question.' The dark shadow moved, becoming an extremely tall, wide-shouldered young man, his breadth magnified by a casual leather jacket worn atop tight-fitting suede trousers.

'I'm Mr. Craig's secretary,' she said, 'and I have a right to be here. Who are you?'

'I have an appointment with Mr. Craig,' the man replied, ignoring her question.

Amanda looked at him suspiciously. It was nearer seven than six, and she had been in this very room when Mr. Craig had agreed to meet Mr. Foster at six-thirty. 'Are you sure you haven't mistaken the time or the day? Mr. Craig has already left.'

'The devil he has!' The man strode to the desk and Amanda sidestepped in front of him. If he thought he

51

was going to look through Mr. Craig's papers he had better think again.

'If you would like to leave a message for Mr. Craig, I'll see he gets it in the morning.' She spoke more calmly than she felt, for the visitor looked extremely irate, his brows drawn together in a frown, his eyes so narrowed that she could not see their colour. But there was no doubt about the colour of his hair: it was as vividly red as her own.

'Who shall I tell him called?' she asked.

'Red.'

'The pot shouldn't call the kettle,' she said with asperity.

'I beg your pardon?'

Only as she saw his eyebrows lift did she realise he had been answering her question and not making a comment on her own hair. She blushed furiously, and seeing it, he understood what she had meant and grinned, showing brilliant white teeth.

'You thought I was getting at you, eh? You couldn't be more wrong, Miss—er——?'

'Miss Stewart.'

'Miss Stewart. The one thing my own hair has taught me is never to tease anyone else about it.' He flexed an arm and she saw the muscles bulge. 'Turned me into the school boxing champion, though. I assume it didn't do the same for you?'

'That's hardly likely.' She could not help smiling, and he seemed to look at her for the first time. What he saw obviously pleased him, for he perched on the edge of the desk and swung one long leg as he surveyed her with deliberate thoroughness from top to toe.

Knowing she would either have to walk out or stand

her ground, Amanda remained where she was and returned his appraisal with equal candour. In his highly fashionable but markedly casual clothes, he did not look the sort of man with whom Gordon Craig was likely to have an appointment, yet she was sure he was not lying. There was too much assurance in his manner, too calm a look on his face. It was a nice face, she decided, with a clear skin used to outdoor life, vivid blue eyes and a cleft chin. If it were not for his awful red hair he would be very good-looking.

'Well?' he drawled. 'Do I meet with your approval? You certainly meet with mine!'

She snorted, 'I don't like red hair.'

'Lucky for me I don't have the same objections. I find yours particularly beautiful.'

'Shall I make another appointment for you to see Mr. Craig?' she asked, ignoring his comment.

'No, thanks, I'll phone him at home tonight, or do you think he'll be back? I don't mind waiting.'

'He never said anything about coming back, but I doubt it. He had an appointment with Mr. Foster.'

'Is that what he told you?'

'I heard him make the arrangements.' She spoke stiffly. 'I got the impression he was going over to the head office to see him at six-thirty.'

The man gave an exclamation of annoyance and stood up. 'Then there's no point in my waiting.' He looked at her with interest. 'Are you staying behind for any reason?'

Annoyed at the guilty colour that flooded into her cheeks, she shook her head. 'I was just leaving.'

'Then we can go down in the lift together.' He leaned against the doorway while she powdered her nose and put on a coat, then loped beside her as she headed for the lift.

At close quarters, he towered above her, and she wondered nervously if he had really come to see Mr. Craig or was an intruder looking for money. A few girls had reported things stolen from their desks in the past few days.

'Have you come to see Mr. Craig for any particular reason? Perhaps I could help you,' she said in her most matter-of-fact voice. 'It might save you making another appointment.'

'Competent though you undoubtedly are, I'm afraid only Mr. Craig can help me. In case I don't manage to get him this evening, perhaps you would be kind enough to tell him I'll call him in the morning about ten.'

'He always meets the buyers at that time. If you could call either before or afterwards——'

'I can't,' he said tersely. 'Give him my message and tell him to wait.'

'Really, Mr.——'

Like him she had to hesitate over his name, and as she did so, he grinned and said: 'Clark. Red Clark.'

'I'll give him your message, Mr. Clark.' Each word tinkled like ice. 'But I can't promise he'll be in for your call.'

'Care to bet on it?'

'I don't bet.'

'If you're so sure he won't wait for me, it wouldn't *be* a bet. It would be a certainty!'

Angrily she rounded on him. 'Very well, what stake shall it be? Ten pence, fifty pence?' Then recklessly: 'A pound if you like.'

'Make it dinner.'

'I beg your pardon?'

'If Mr. Craig waits for my call I'll expect you to have dinner with me tomorrow night.'

'Of all the ridiculous ... Certainly not!'

'Welching on a bet? I never expected it of you, Miss Stewart. You just agreed to let me name the stake.'

'I was thinking in terms of money, not dinner.'

'Dinner would be far more expensive for me than a pound.' He looked down at her speculatively, his blue eyes gleaming. 'Unless you'd be satisfied with a roll and butter!'

'I wouldn't be satisfied anywhere with you, Mr. Clark.'

'Then you *are* welching on the bet.'

'I'm not!' she said furiously.

'Very well then,' he said as the lift doors opened and they stepped into the hall, 'I'll pick you up here tomorrow evening at the same time.' He held open the main door for her. 'Don't bother getting dressed up. You look lovely the way you are.'

Ignoring her exclamation of fury, he waved good-bye and made his way to the vintage sports car that was the sole occupant of the car park. Without bothering to open the door, he put his long legs over the side and settled into the bucket seat.

'Until tomorrow night,' he called, and with a loud revving of the engine, roared away.

Not until she was telling her mother what had happened did Amanda see the funny side of the situation.

'We'd look like twins if we went out together. Can you imagine it? One carrot-top is bad enough, but two together ...!'

'I wish you wouldn't be so derogatory about your hair. I think it's beautiful and so does Mr. Brand.'

The knowledge made Amanda brighten, but later

that evening as she sat watching the television, she remembered that Red Clark's arrival at the office had prevented her from looking at the piece of paper she had torn from the note-pad. As an exercise in commercial espionage she had abysmally failed the first test.

She was at the office early the next morning and waiting by Mr. Craig's desk when he arrived.

'Someone called to see you last night,' she said, helping him off with his coat. 'A Mr. Clark.'

'Who?'

'Clark.' So she was right, Amanda thought, he had been a burglar. 'Red Clark,' she repeated.

'Red?' Mr. Craig's face was a study in consternation. 'You mean he came *here*?'

'Yes. He said he had an appointment with you.'

An unusually strong epithet was her employer's comment as he marched over and took his place at the desk. 'I didn't realise he was coming here. I was supposed to meet him at ...' Mr. Craig frowned. 'Did he saying anything else?'

'Only that he'd call you at ten o'clock this morning. I told him you always have a meeting at that time, but he refused to ring at any other.'

Mr. Craig grunted, with which unsatisfactory answer Amanda had to be satisfied.

For the next half hour she was kept busy with the morning post, but as ten o'clock arrived she was on tenterhooks and kept glancing at her watch and praying for Mr. Craig to begin his meeting. But ten o'clock came and he made no move to do so. At ten-fifteen he was still alone in the office and her agitation rose. At ten-twenty his telephone rang, and with a premonition Amanda knew who it was.

'Ah, Mr. Clark,' said Gordon Craig smoothly, and nodded to Amanda to leave him alone.

Wishing she could bang the door behind her, Amanda returned to her office. But here her anger gave way to curiosity. The morning meeting with the buyers was a regular ritual, and Red Clark must be extremely important if Mr. Craig would delay it in order to wait for his call. She glanced at the two telephones on her desk. The red one had a light glowing, which meant her employer was still speaking. Whatever it was Mr. Clark wanted to discuss, it was taking a long time. Impatiently she waited for the light to go out, but it was fifteen minutes before it did so, and her buzzer immediately sounded to call her back into the office.

'Sorry about the interruption,' Mr. Craig apologised. 'If Mr. Clark should call at any other time, always put him straight through to me.'

'Does he work for the organisation?' she asked without expression.

'Yes.'

'What does he do?'

If he was surprised by the question Mr. Craig did not show it. 'He's an estate agent.'

'He doesn't look like one. Last night he looked more like a burglar.'

A slight smile passed over Gordon Craig's face. 'Mr. Clark is rather partial to casual clothes. He's out of his office so much that he can wear what he likes.'

It was not so much her employer's words as the tone in which he uttered them that gave Amanda the feeling he was hiding something. Not that it was difficult to guess what it was. Red Clark obviously helped Homefare to find sites for their new stores, and as such he was important to them. No wonder he had been confident Mr. Craig would wait for his call. The point of her pencil snapped as she unconsciously dug it into her pad. The telephone call! She had lost her bet.

'Is anything wrong, Miss Stewart?' her employer enquired.

She shook her head, her thoughts racing with her own affairs even while she took dictation. She had no intention of keeping her date with that red-haired know-all. The only way to avoid him was to leave early. If she was not given any last-minute letters and she stayed behind in her lunch-hour, it should be possible to go by five.

Luck was with her. A meeting with a buyer from Kelloggs took Mr. Craig out of the office from lunch-time onwards, and with barely a quarter of her note-book filled, she was able to complete her work well before five. Nervously she kept glancing through the window, but there was no sign of the vintage sports car, and with a thrill of triumph she put on her coat, tied a chiffon scarf around her head and sped down the stairs.

'You're off early,' the porter called as she ran across the marble floor.

'I worked through my lunch-hour.'

'Rushing to meet your young man, eh?' he grinned.

'Rushing to avoid him!' she grinned back, and pushing through the revolving glass doors, ran straight into the arms of the man she was trying to escape. 'You!' she gasped.

'In the flesh! I didn't know you were so eager to see me you'd come rushing out ahead of time. Or were you trying to leave before I got here?' He held her away from him but did not let her go, his hands gripping her arms like two vices. Her expression gave him his answer. 'Naughty, naughty,' he said gently, and gave her a shake that set her teeth rattling. 'Beautiful little girls should be prepared to pay their debts.'

'I'd be more than happy to pay it in money,' she said bitterly, 'but having to spend an evening with you ... Really, Mr. Clark, it's ridiculous. We don't even know each other.'

'We'll soon remedy that.'

Still holding her, he frogmarched her to his car and opened the door for her to get in.

With as much dignity as she could muster, she did so, then smoothed down her hair, wishing it were as easy to do the same with her feelings. She could not remember the last time she had been so angry.

'Relax,' he murmured. 'You should remember the old saying: if you can't fight 'em, join 'em.'

She refused to answer and stared resolutely out of the window. To her surprise Red Clark drove carefully, not abusing the enormous power hidden beneath the long bonnet, and she snuggled lower and re-knotted her scarf against the wind.

'You're cold,' he said, and switched on the dashboard. There was a whining sound and the winter daylight grew darker as a black leather hood glided automatically into place, enclosing them snugly.

'I didn't think an old car like this would have an automatic roof,' she exclaimed.

'I fitted it myself. Daisy here may be an old jalopy,' he tapped the wheel, 'but she's got all the mod. cons.!'

He pressed another switch and a blast of hot air blew against Amanda's skirt. She crossed her legs quickly, wishing she was wearing something more feminine than a navy dress; not that she had any need to impress this egotistical man. She glanced at him and saw he was as casually dressed as yesterday, though this time his sweater was the same blue as his eyes. As blue as her own, she thought, and could not help smiling at the way they must look together.

'We could be twins,' she said before she could stop herself.

'The closeness of the idea appeals to me, but not the relationship!'

Her mouth quirked, but she refused to smile. He seemed unperturbed by her lack of response and whistled tunelessly beneath his breath, not bothering to make conversation. They were in the thick of the rush-hour traffic and she saw they were heading east towards the river. Expecting him to be impatient at the snarl-up, she was surprised by his unconcern, and he inched forward cheerfully, allowing several cars to press ahead of him.

'It's not worth getting an ulcer over,' he said when she commented on his giving way to one particularly aggressive driver. 'When I ever do blow my top, it's over something that matters.'

They were now coming out of the traffic and, leaving the city behind, she found the streets becoming wider and more deserted, with row after row of council flats: grey blocks of concrete pointing dismal fingers into the sky.

'There are no restaurants down here,' she said suspiciously. 'Where are you taking me?'

'Not to the Savoy.'

'I wasn't expecting it,' she said indignantly. 'But I don't intend to go to Bert's Café either!'

He laughed outright. 'Ladies go where they're taken. But don't worry, radish-head, I can promise you you'll like the food.'

'Don't call me radish-head!' She turned upon him angrily. 'I didn't want to come out with you, Mr. Clark, so the very least you can do is to be civil.'

'No offence intended. I just thought you'd prefer it to being called Carrots.'

'I'd prefer to be called nothing,' she said between clenched teeth. 'This whole evening with you is going to be a disaster.'

'That's what I like about you,' he said equably. 'Your optimism and your great trusting quality. I noticed it last night in the office, when you couldn't quite make up your mind if I'd come to rape you or to steal the stamps!'

'I'm still not sure!'

He chuckled. 'When you're angry, your hair glows like copper. How about my calling you Copper-Knob? Or is that verboten too?'

'If you——' She choked and stopped, and he resumed talking as if she had not tried to interrupt him.

'Mind you, I only tease girls I'm fond of. If you really do have a thing about your hair I'll call you plain Amanda.' He gave her a teasing look. 'I'm sure you've already been called beautiful Amanda.'

'Yes, I have.'

'By anyone special?'

'The man who wants to marry me.'

'From that answer I take it you don't want to marry him.'

'Why do you say that?'

'Because you didn't call him your boy-friend.'

'I'm afraid your psychology is at fault, Mr. Clark. As it happens I am seriously considering the proposal.'

'My, my, how formal you make it sound! Lover boy

can't be in *our* generation. Is he your father figure?'

'Oh, shut up!'

'Yes, ma'am.'

Despite herself, she giggled. 'Aren't you ever serious, Mr. Clark?'

'Not if I can help it; and the name's Red—or have you forgotten?'

'With hair like yours it would be impossible to forget.' She bit her lip. 'Now you've got *me* at it!'

'Good. I knew you'd be my sort of girl once you relaxed.'

He swung the car round a corner and down a narrow winding street, stopping it outside a small restaurant. The window was curtained and there was no name above it, but inside it was spotless, with half a dozen tables covered with snow white linen.

'Mr. Clark—delighted to see you again.' A dapper little man with a bald head greeted them and led them to a corner table.

'What can you recommend tonight, Solly?'

'Everything. You know this place, Mr. Clark. Nothing's stale here. How about the salt beef? It's always your favourite, and Milly is doing the *latkes* now.'

Red looked at Amanda. 'Those are potato pancakes; but unlike anything you've ever tasted.'

'What's salt beef?' she asked warily.

'Beef that's been pickled and then boiled. Try it. It's very tasty.' He glanced at the proprietor. 'Soup to begin with, with those unpronounceable dumplings of yours.'

'*Knaidlach*,' said the proprietor, beaming, and hurried away to complete the order.

As Red had promised, the meal was delicious. Amanda had not tasted Jewish cooking before and she found it had a highly seasoned robustness reminiscent of Italian cookery. The dumplings were particularly good, being a mixture of cornmeal, chicken fat and ground almonds. The dessert was equally succulent: a syrupy almond pudding with fresh apricots.

'How did you find this place?' she asked, sipping black coffee. Milk, it seemed, was not served after a menu that consisted of meat.

'Homefare wanted to extend one of their super-markets and Solly had his restaurant next door. They bought him out and I promised I'd find him other premises—which I did. I've kept in touch with him ever since. He's delighted with this new place of his.'

'He's one of the lucky ones,' Amanda said bitterly.

'*He* thinks so. He got an excellent price for his lease and was able to buy this restaurant and put a sizeable bit into the bank at the same time.'

'Generous Homefare!'

His look was sharp. 'Do I detect real feeling in that remark?'

'My father didn't find them quite so generous,' she said tersely.

'Tell me.'

'It's a boring story.'

'Nothing about you is boring.' He rested his elbows on the table. 'Tell me, Amanda.'

Impelled by his interest, she did so, and he listened in silence until she finished.

'Aren't you being over-critical of Homefare?' he asked finally. 'They did offer to buy out your father in the beginning. You can't blame them for not want-ing to do so afterwards.'

'I don't blame them for that,' she retorted. 'I blame them for making it impossible for the ordinary shopkeeper to earn a living.'

'People won't pay more for food than they have to.'

'How can a man with one shop compete with a supermarket who can buy food in huge quantities?'

'They can't. They either give in or go in for speciality items. You'll always find a nucleus of people willing to pay more for extra service and the unusual commodity.'

'Not in a little country village.'

'That was just bad luck on your father's part; but you shouldn't let it sour you against Homefare.' He looked quizzical. 'After all, you're working for them yourself.' He leaned closer to her. 'How long have you been with the company?'

'Not long. I worked for—for Brands before.'

'The redoubtable Clive Brand.'

'You know him?' she asked, surprised.

He grinned. 'Do I look the type who would?'

'No, you don't.' It was on the tip of her tongue to tell him that *she* did, but something held her back, and as she lay in bed later that night she wondered why. All she knew was that she had experienced a strange reluctance to tell him that someone so wealthy had asked her to marry him. Not that Red Clark would have been abashed by it. She had never met anyone so sure of himself nor so uninterested in seeing her again. Anticipating that he would wish to do so, she had mentally rehearsed her refusal, and had been disconcertingly piqued at not being given the opportunity of airing it for, depositing her at her front door at midnight, he had thanked her for a lovely evening and driven away. Obviously he had only been interested in having her pay her bet; that done, it seemed the end as far as he was concerned.

'And a good thing too,' she decided, thumping her pillow into another position, and refused to admit that she felt even the slightest sense of disappointment.

CHAPTER FIVE

THE following evening Amanda saw Clive. She had arranged to go straight to his home and refused his offer to send his car and chauffeur for her.

'If any of the other girls see me getting into a Rolls,' she explained, 'they'll start asking me questions.'

'So what?'

'So I don't want to be met.'

'I don't like you strap-hanging in a bus or fighting to get into the subway. At least promise me you'll take a taxi.'

Dutifully agreeing to do so she replaced the receiver. Not even to herself would she admit the reason she did not want Clive to send his car for her, though as she left the office late that afternoon and looked around warily, albeit with great care, for the sight of a lanky, red-haired figure, she could no longer avoid acknowledging the reason. But there was no sign of Red, and angry with herself for having expected him, she strode smartly to the station, forgetting her promise to Clive to take a taxi.

It was not until she entered his elegant drawing-rom that her irritation ebbed, and because his tender greeting was balm to her pride, she gave him a far warmer kiss than usual. At once he pulled her closer and kissed her again, his mouth unusually demanding. The passion of it took her by surprise and she tried to respond, but she was conscious of stupid little details that made it impossible to lose herself in his embrace: the buttons of his suit dug painfully into her breast, her head was tilted back at an uncomfortable angle, and the sharp smell of his shaving lotion tickled her nostrils.

Aware of her lack of response, he let her go. 'You're tired. I'll get you a drink.'

As she had expected, there was champagne on ice and a silver dish of delicious canapés. A smile tugged at her mouth. Champagne and caviar tonight, chicken soup and dumplings yesterday! No one could say she was not a girl who went to extremes.

'What's amusing you?' he asked.

'I'm smiling at the way you spoil me,' she lied, accepting a glass of champagne and drawing a chair close to the fire.

'I thought we'd have dinner here,' he said, 'unless you'd prefer to go out?'

'I'm happy to do whatever you prefer.'

'That's one of your nicest characteristics. You don't make demands. You'll make a wonderful wife.'

'Is that your criterion for a wonderful wife?'

'She would have to have other qualities too. But being reasonable is the most important.' He sat down opposite her and gave her a tender smile. 'Don't look so mutinous, darling. I'm sure you and I will agree over all the major decisions we have to make.'

'What would happen if I—if your wife didn't?' Amanda asked.

'We'd talk it out. All problems can be solved by discussion.' His smile grew nervous. 'Are you trying to tell me you've made up your mind?'

'No,' she said hastily, 'I'm not. I mean I haven't.

Don't rush me, Clive. You promised you wouldn't.'

'So my nightmare continues.'

There was such pathos in the remark that she gave a little murmur and ran over to him. 'I don't want to hurt you, Clive. I'll tell you the minute I can.'

He drew her hand to his lips, making no move to drop it when the butler came in to say dinner was ready. With servants waiting on them throughout the meal, their conversation was superficial, but when they were alone again Clive asked her how she had spent her day, and sensing a deeper meaning behind his question, she shrugged noncommittally and waited for him to say more.

'Have you heard any news about more sites?' he continued.

'Not a thing. Mr. Craig doesn't talk much when I'm around.'

'You do his letters, though, and there are inter-office memos.'

'Not many. When the executives have anything to say they ring each other up. It's not like Brands, where everything has to be typed out in triplicate!'

He smiled. 'I take it you didn't approve of that custom?'

'You wouldn't either, if you had to do the typing!'

'If something is written down there can be no mistake about it—unlike a telephone conversation. Homefare are well known for being disorderly.'

'It isn't reflected in their profits.' She saw his sharp look and flushed. 'I'm sorry, Clive, that was a spiteful thing to say.'

'I don't mind a spark or two.' There was a twinkle in his eye which made him look younger and happier. 'Because I appreciate acquiescence in a woman it

67

doesn't mean I like dullness.'

'I think the two often go together.'

'You're not dull,' he retorted, 'but I've always found you amenable!'

'Wait until you ask me to do something I don't want to do.'

'I'm too clever to do that. I never ask anyone to do anything unless I know they'll agree.'

'How can you be so sure?'

'Instinct.'

'Like choosing the right site?'

'Exactly. I have confidence in my judgment and my ability. That doesn't mean I'm conceited, Amanda. The gifts I have come from God, and I'm grateful for them. Nonetheless I recognise them and know how to use them.'

Listening to him, Amanda marvelled at his self-confidence, and wondered wistfully if any of it would rub off on her if she married him. Not that she would need to do any pushing if she were his wife. To Mrs. Clive Brand all doors would be open.

'You must have worked hard to get where you are,' she said. 'And you still do.'

'I enjoy it. I like pitting my wits against other people —always being a jump ahead of them.'

'You aren't doing too well at the moment.'

'Homefare's a special case,' he retorted stiffly. 'Charles Foster isn't the sort of man one usually comes up against. He's irrational and difficult.'

'Sounds like a typical tycoon to me—present company excluded!'

'He isn't at all typical. He's exactly the contrary. He makes a joke of everything—and because of it, one can never gauge his mood.'

'Then I'd call him a clever man, not an irrational one.'

Clive raised his eyebrows and pulled in his lower lip. 'You may well be right,' he said slowly. 'Perhaps the man's even deeper than I thought.'

'Do you know him well?'

'As well as one can ever know him.'

'Mr. Craig said he was a loner.'

'The description fits him.'

Clive still looked pensive and Amanda knew an urge to please him. 'I'll try to find out what I can about any new sites. I haven't forgotten I said I would.'

'Never mind, darling, I'm sure you'll get an opportunity.'

Clive reached out and drew her on to his lap.

For a moment she found it difficult to relax, part of her mind looking down on herself as though she were two separate people. How could Amanda Stewart be surrendering to the kisses of a man whose name was a byword to millions of housewives? Then the two sections of her mind fused and she was again the slender redhead into whose ear a man was whispering words of love.

'I want to give you so much, my darling,' Clive said passionately. 'You'll be the best dressed woman in the world, and the most beautiful.' His hand caressed her throat. 'I've already ordered pearls for you. You must always wear pearls! They were made for a skin like yours.'

She would not have been human if she had not been bemused by such words, and she twined her arms around his neck. How easy it would be to give him the answer he wanted. She opened her mouth to do so, but he saw her parted lips as an invitation and covered them with his own. She instinctively tried to resist, but whereas on other occasions he had let her go, tonight he ignored her resistance and went on kissing her, his hands moving over her body with firm assurance, their warmth penetrating her woollen dress. It was only as his fingers fumbled at the buttons of her bodice that she pushed his hands away, and jumped to her feet.

'No, Clive, I can't!'

Head leaning back on the settee, he surveyed her. 'I would never go further than you wanted. You have no need to be afraid of me.'

'I'm afraid of myself.'

His eyes widened. 'That's the nicest thing you've said to me. Perhaps we should have a few more sessions like this.'

Laughing, she backed away from his outstretched arms, pleading the lateness of the hour and the pressures of the following day.

'I'll take you home,' he said, conceding her the victory. 'But you might not win next time!'

As usual Clive saw Amanda to her front door, but this time he suggested coming in for a cup of coffee and a chat with her mother. Hiding her surprise, she took him up to the flat. She had got over her embarrassment at living here, though some of it returned as she saw how incongruous he looked in the small sitting-room, his faultlessly tailored figure making the settee and curtains look lumpy and ill-cut.

As she made coffee in the kitchenette she heard her mother and Clive talking, though Clive seemed to be doing most of it, a sure sign that her mother was still uneasy with him. Quickly she poured out the coffee and went in to join them.

'I was just telling your mother I would like you both

to spend the summer at my house in Vancouver,' Clive said as he took his cup. 'It's so much like England that English people always feel at home there.'

'If I went as far away as that,' Mrs. Stewart smiled, 'I'd at least like to feel I was in a foreign country!'

'Then you'll be pleased to know I'm looking for a house in France. Perhaps you'd prefer to be there?'

'I don't think I have the right to prefer either!'

'When Amanda's my wife——' He stopped and flung Amanda an apologetic look. 'Sorry, dear, I keep forgetting you haven't said yes.'

'You haven't forgotten at all,' Amanda said. 'You're trying to bulldoze me into saying yes!'

'Do you blame me?'

'No, but you'll only make me obstinate. I haven't got red hair for nothing.'

He sipped his coffee and appraised her. 'I often think about your hair. You should always wear green or blue.'

'Everyone always says that to redheads.'

'Because they're the two most becoming colours.' He set down his empty cup. 'You both look tired. I don't want to outstay my welcome.'

Downstairs in the hall he caught Amanda's hand. 'I'm going to Newcastle tomorrow and I won't be back until the day after, but keep the weekend free, won't you?'

'Would you be cross if I didn't?'

'Not cross—disappointed.'

'Then I promise not to disappoint you.'

Arriving at the office the next morning she was surprised to find Mr. Craig already at his desk, his eyes red-rimmed with fatigue, and notebooks and papers scattered around him.

'You look as if you didn't sleep much last night.'

'I didn't. We've just signed a contract to build a hypermarket outside Watford. I was up all night working out the figures.'

'Figures for what?'

'The highest costs we might have to meet. I take the number of people in the area and their estimated buying capacity; then I work out running costs and try to assess the minimum and maximum size we can go to and still show a profit.' He jabbed at a page of notes. 'Unfortunately Mr. Foster wants this hypermarket to be the biggest in the country, and no matter what figures I produce, he'll dispute them.'

'Then make up any figure,' Amanda said lightly.

'And lose my job?'

'How would Mr. Foster know they weren't accurate? He isn't Superman!'

'I'm not so sure!'

Amanda pulled a face. 'What's he like? I was hoping I would see him when I worked here, but I've never even caught sight of him.'

'You'll meet him one day.' Mr. Craig shuffled his papers together. 'If you'd like to bring in your notebook. . . .'

Amanda did as she was told, and no sooner was she seated than he began to dictate such a complicated set of figures that she had to stop several times to make sure she was getting them down correctly.

'I'd better rough type them out and let you check them,' she said when he came to the end.

'A good idea. But when you type them properly don't put the carbons in the file. *I'll* take them. Our competitors would give a great deal to see these figures.'

Amanda went scarlet and Mr. Craig immediately looked apologetic. 'I wasn't suggesting I don't trust you, Miss Stewart, but Mr. Foster made that rule a long while ago.'

'I understand,' she said stiffly, and hurried out before he could apologise again.

How horrified he would be if he knew he had good reason to be suspicious of her. The facts and figures he had dictated would be of enormous value to Clive. No one would be any the wiser if she made a carbon copy for herself. But she dared not do that. It would be too risky. Mr. Craig had a habit of coming into her office without warning and might see it. But there was nothing to stop her jotting the figures down in her diary. Not giving herself a chance to change her mind, she took it out of her handbag.

It was only as she went to turn over the pages of her shorthand book that the horror of what she was doing came home to her. It was one thing to tell Clive of the conversations she overheard, but quite another to deliberately copy out material which she knew to be highly confidential.

With shaking hands she put away her diary and got rid of her nerves by pounding on the typewriter. No matter how much she disliked Homefare it was impossible to spy on them. Her father's face came clearly into her mind as she had seen him a bare hour before he had been killed. How much wiser he would have been to have accepted the first offer Homefare had made to him. Her hands dropped from the typewriter and she stared into space. This was the first time she had thought such a thing, and though she felt she was being disloyal to her father's memory, she knew she could not ignore the truth any longer. It had been unworldly of him to think he could compete with such a massive group. If their shop had been in the wealthy stockbroker belt he might have had some reason for his optimism, but it had been in a farming community where the saving of a few pence was all-important. If her father had realised this he would be alive today, either working as a manager for Homefare, or living on their original generous offer; for that it was generous she could no longer deny.

With a sigh she resumed work. Soon the figures and details were set out and she took the pages in to Mr. Craig. Surprisingly there were no errors, and she was asked to retype them and make a copy.

Unwilling to have the figures lying around her desk, she did so immediately, delaying her lunch until she was able to take the pages back to Mr. Craig.

'Here are my shorthand notes too,' she said. 'I would like you to tear them up. Then you won't be worried about anyone getting the information.'

'Please, Miss Stewart,' Mr. Craig looked uncomfortable. 'I've already apologised.'

'I know, and I didn't mean it that way. It's just that I prefer you to tear the pages for *my* peace of mind.'

He did so, and dropped the shreds into the wastepaper basket.

'What will happen to the figures now?' she asked.

'Mr. Foster will check them out with the other directors and then go ahead with what he intended to do in the first place!'

'I'm darned if I would have bothered,' she said warmly.

'When the Chairman asks for details. . . .' His private line rang and he picked up the receiver. 'Talk of the devil,' he murmured, and said no more until Amanda left the room.

She was still thinking about the ploys of business when she left the office at the end of the day. It had been an unusually strenuous one, for despite the fact that he had been up for most of the night, Mr. Craig worked with unusual intensity, giving her so much dictation that it would take her several days to type it back. Her fingers were still aching as she pushed the revolving door and stepped out into the damp night air. It was raining slightly and the pavements were wet and gleaming, the edges of the street lamps misty from the moisture-laden atmosphere. How quickly winter set in once the autumn leaves had fallen. Burying her chin in the collar of her coat, she set off in the direction of the subway. She had hardly taken two steps when a firm arm came around her waist and it did not need the words: 'Hallo, Copper-Knob,' to tell her it was Red Clark.

Her heart beat so fast that she found it difficult to speak. 'What—what are you doing here?'

'I should have thought that was obvious. I've been waiting for you.'

'Why?'

'You're very dumb tonight!' Still holding her, he guided her towards his car, walking so fast that she was forced to run in order to keep up with him.

'I can't go with you,' she protested. 'I'm going home.'

'I'm taking you out to dinner.'

'No, you're not.'

He stopped so abruptly that she knocked against him, and as she hastily went to draw back, she found his other arm stopping her. 'Do you have a date with another man?' he demanded.

75

'No,' she said, being truthful before she could stop herself, 'but my mother's expecting me.'

'Ring her and say you'll be late.'

'I don't want to. I was out last night and I don't like leaving her alone too often.' His look was questioning and she felt it necessary to explain. 'My mother isn't well and my father's death is still so recent that——'

'You needn't say any more,' Red interrupted. 'I should have realised it myself. But it doesn't constitute a major problem, you know. We'll buy some food and have dinner at *your* place.'

'We can't do that.'

'Give me one good reason why not.'

The glint in the piercing blue eyes decided her against trying. If she knew nothing else about this self-willed man, she at least knew that he was obstinate. Taking her silence as acquiescence, he bundled her into the car.

'Any particular preference for food?' he asked, and when she shook her head said no more. For a man who liked to tease he could be remarkably taciturn. She glanced at him and amended the thought; not taciturn. He just had nothing to say and did not want to make small talk.

The car slid to a stop outside a restaurant in Soho and Amanda looked at him reproachfully.

'I told you I couldn't have dinner with you.'

'Oh, ye of little faith!' he grinned, clambering out of the car. 'But if you can't come to the dinner, the dinner will come to you! Now sit quiet. I'll be as quick as I can.'

Within a surprisingly short time he emerged from the restaurant, followed by two waiters, each carrying a basket which they placed carefully in the boot of the car, grinning their thanks as they were lavishly tipped.

'You shouldn't have gone to the expense of buying a proper meal,' she said as they drove away. 'I had no idea you were going to do anything like that.'

'I can afford it, Copper-Knob.'

'You don't look all that affluent.' Aware of his grin, she tossed her head. 'Your car is old and you don't dress as if.... Oh, you know what I mean.'

'Indeed I do. But don't be fooled by appearances. I'm not short of a bob or two. Still, I'm touched by your concern. I'd hate to think you were a gold-digger.'

She was warmed by the teasing compliment, and felt unaccountably happy as, a short while later, she preceded Red up the stairs to her flat.

Only as she turned the key in the lock did she remember she had not given her mother any warning that she was bringing someone back with her and—equally important—someone who did not know of her friendship with Clive Brand. Quickly she ushered Red into the sitting-room and then hurried to find her mother.

Mrs. Stewart was in the bedroom tidying her hair. 'I heard a car draw up outside and thought you'd come back with Clive,' she explained.

'He's gone to Newcastle. It's Red who's here—the estate agent I told you about. The one who works for Homefare.'

'Is he taking you out?'

'In a way,' Amanda giggled. 'He's brought a restaurant dinner here—for all of us!'

Mrs. Stewart looked astonished. 'Why ever did he do that?'

'I told him I intended staying in with you.'

'He sounds a resourceful young man.'

77

'You can say that again! Now come in and meet him, but don't mention Clive.'

'Of course not.' Her mother was tranquil. 'One never talks to one suitor about another.'

'Red isn't my suitor,' Amanda exclaimed.

'Of course not,' the answer came again, and with an old-fashioned look at her daughter's pink cheeks, Mrs. Stewart went out.

There was no doubt Red had a way with older women, Amanda decided a couple of hours later as she watched her mother laughing at one of his ridiculous jokes. In fact it would be difficult for anyone not to be at ease with him, for he had a facility for appearing interested in everyone he met.

At nine-thirty he stood up to leave and, surprised by his wanting to go so early, she went with him to the downstairs door.

'I don't want to leave,' he explained, 'but your mother looks tired, and even if she had gone to bed she wouldn't have slept while I was still here.'

'You're very knowledgeable about mothers!'

'I make it my business to be!'

'And you're conceited too.'

'I know my worth,' he grinned. 'I'm sorry for anyone who doesn't.'

'Not all of us have your kind of confidence.'

'*You* should have stacks of it.' His eyes gleamed. 'You're not a bad-looking girl.'

'Thanks.'

Head on one side, he surveyed her. The bright light in the hall shone full on his hair, making it glow no less vividly than her own. 'You're a bit too thin for some people's taste, but you appeal to mine; and you have an extremely kissable mouth.'

Quickly she drew back, but she was not quick enough for him. His arms came tightly around her and he pulled her close.

'Very kissable,' he repeated, and proceeded to prove he meant what he said.

Red Clark might have a casual manner, but there was nothing casual in the way he kissed. There was passion and intensity in it, and after a long, exploring moment she felt herself responding to him. Aware of it, he drew her closer still, and one long, lean leg twined itself between hers. He did not speak, but the occasional tremor that went through him communicated itself to her, and she had no need to see the tight look around his mouth when he finally pushed her away from him, to know he was holding himself firmly in check.

'I've never yet seduced a girl in a hallway,' he said jerkily, 'but there's always a first time. Get thee behind me, Satan!'

He opened the front door, gave her a wave and went out.

Surprised by his quick departure, she stood waiting. A car door slammed, an engine roared and then there was silence. He had not said a word about seeing her again, nor made any mention of calling her. Forcing her mind into a blank, she went upstairs.

Her determination to forget Red Clark was not put to the test, for when she awoke the next morning it was to find that her mother had a temperature of a hundred and three, and this put everything else out of her mind.

'I popped out last night to get an evening paper,' Mrs. Stewart croaked by way of explanation, 'and got caught in the rain. I was going to change when you and Red came home.'

'Then you deserve to have a cold,' Amanda said crossly, using her irritation to hide her fear. 'I'll telephone the office and let them know I won't be in this morning. I'd like the doctor to come and see you.'

'It's only a chill.'

'Better to be safe than sorry,' said Amanda, and remembered these words when the doctor diagnosed pneumonia and said her mother must be sent to hospital.

'I've already asked the emergency bed service to see what they can do,' he said, 'but it won't be easy at this time of the year. They'll let you know as soon as they find a bed. I doubt if it will be close at hand, but in a case like this your mother will have to go where they send her.'

Amanda nodded, though she did not relish the prospect of a daily journey to the other side of London.

'Let me know to which hospital she's sent,' the doctor said, picking up his bag, 'and give the ambulance man this note.'

Amanda took it and returned to the bedroom. Hardly had she done so than the telephone rang and she rushed to answer it. But it was Clive calling to say he had returned from Newcastle earlier than he had expected. At once he sensed something was wrong.

'It's my mother,' she said tearfully, and told him what had happened.

'Stop worrying, darling,' he said, 'and leave everything to me. If the Emergency Service calls you, tell them you've already made arrangements.'

'What arrangements?'

'I'll call you back and let you know.'

His orders as to what she should say proved needless, for he telephoned her again before they did. 'An ambulance is on its way to you. I've got your mother into the Downshire Clinic.' He named London's most exclusive private hospital. 'I've also spoken to my own doctor and he'll be at Downshire by the time you arrive there.'

'But I—you shouldn't have done it,' she stammered. 'I never expected it.'

'You *should* have expected it.' There was rebuke in his tone. 'I love you, Amanda. Don't you know I'll do everything in my power to help you?'

Guiltier than ever, she stammered an apology, but he cut her short.

'I don't want your thanks,' he interrupted, 'but next time anything goes wrong with you, I hope you'll remember that I'm here to help you.'

Unable to say anything for tears, Amanda went to tell her mother what had happened, but Mrs. Stewart seemed unaware of what was going on around her and though Amanda knew high temperatures could cause delirium, she was nonetheless frightened by it.

It seemed an eternity before the ambulance arrived. But once she saw the efficient attendants her fear lessened.

'It's always worrying to see someone delirious,' one of the men told her. 'But it's amazing how quickly a temperature can be brought down these days.'

The words were proved correct, for by early afternoon Amanda found it hard to believe that the horror of the morning had taken place. Lying in a high white bed in a cheerful, flower-filled room in the clinic, Mrs. Stewart looked far better able to fight for her life than four hours ago, and Amanda knew that had it not been for Clive's generous offer to help them, her mother would still be waiting to be admitted to hospital.

At six o'clock she went down to find Clive in the waiting room. He was talking to a middle-aged man whom she had already met when he had come to examine her mother. He smiled at her now and included her in the conversation.

'I was explaining to Mr. Brand that it's quite usual for virus pneumonia to strike without warning. The main thing is to avoid any other complications.'

Amanda shivered and Clive put his arm around her. 'What are my mother's chances?'

'Quite good. We're doing everything possible, Miss Stewart, I can assure you of that.'

They were not the most comforting words she had heard, but she appreciated their honesty.

'I'm not going to leave here,' she told Clive as soon as they were alone. 'I want to be within call.'

'You have to eat, my dear. I've booked a table at a restaurant in South Audley Street. We'll leave the phone number at the desk on our way out. If necessary we can be back here in five minutes.'

Appreciating his thoughtfulness, she did not have the heart to refuse to go with him, and though she remained unaware of what she was eating, she had to admit she felt less tense by the time they drove back to the clinic.

'I'd better tell Mr. Craig to find a temporary,' she said, thinking aloud. 'He won't like it. He's terribly busy at the moment.'

'The usual Homefare excitement and bustle,' Clive commented.

'Not quite usual. They're planning to build the biggest hypermarket in England—outside Watford.'

'You never told me this before.' Clive did not hide his surprise and she was embarrassed by it.

'I thought you already knew,' she stammered.

'I know what their aims are, as far as expansion goes, but I don't know the size of the stores they're planning. They keep that sort of information under wraps. That's where I was hoping *you* could help me.'

'I only heard about the Watford store yesterday, when Mr. Craig showed me the figures for——' Too late she stopped, for Clive had slowed the car and was staring at her.

'The figures for what?'

'Costings. That sort of thing.'

'You had the costings on their new hypermarket?' At her nod he went paler, though he lost none of his composure. 'It's a pity you weren't able to give me a copy.'

'I couldn't. Mr. Craig was in the room the whole time I was typing it out.'

'I see. Well, perhaps you'll have another chance.'

They reached the Downshire and went into the foyer.

'Don't wait here with me,' Amanda said. 'I won't be able to sleep if I go home, so I might as well stay here for the night.'

'I thought that's what you'd do.' His eyes were tender. 'I've arranged for them to give you a room.'

'You think of everything.'

'I enjoy taking care of you.'

'I know, and I can't tell you how grateful I am.'

'Don't use that word. I think of you as if you're my wife.'

The urge to give him the answer he was silently pleading for was so great that she was not sure why she held back. All she knew was that something prevented her from doing so, and with a sigh she kissed him on the cheek and went up to her mother's room.

Later that night as she sat beside her mother's sleeping figure, she wondered why she had not told Clive the real reason she had not given him the costings. Sooner or later she would have to tell him she could not spy on the company for whom she was working. The swift and generous way in which he had come to her aid today made it hard for her not to do as he wanted, but neither her desire to show her gratitude to him, nor her dislike of Homefare, could make her stoop to such behaviour.

The entry of a nurse aroused her from her thoughts, and the girl leaned over her to whisper that she had a visitor downstairs waiting to see her.

Assuming it to be her own doctor, Amanda ran down to the hall, stopping in amazement at the sight of a tall, dark-suited figure whose red hair looked considerably brighter because of the pallor of his skin.

'I waited for you outside the office tonight,' he said before she could speak, 'and when you didn't come out I went round to your flat. Mrs. Chadwalla told me about your mother.' He came forward and roughly caught her arm. 'Why the hell didn't you tell me?'

'How could I? I didn't know where to contact you.'

For the first time since they had met he looked discomfited. 'I'm sorry, Amanda. You're absolutely right. I don't like getting personal calls when I'm working, but I—I'll give you a number where you can always contact me in an emergency.'

Still annoyed at his earlier anger, she was in no mood to be appeased. 'I hope that won't be necessary: and if there are more emergencies, I can manage alone.'

'That seems obvious.'

He looked round the plush foyer and now it was her turn to be discomfited. He must be wondering how she could afford to bring her mother here. 'I couldn't get my mother into a hospital,' she explained, 'and a—a friend of mine arranged for her to come here.'

'The man you can't make up your mind to marry?' His expression was mocking. 'I hope you won't let gratitude influence your decision.'

'Of course I won't.'

He still looked sceptical as he leaned against the wall to look at her. He was casually dressed as always, in dark blue slacks and sweater. It lessened the vividness of his hair, and for some reason it made him look older and more serious, though the seriousness might be coming from his expression which was now unusually sombre as his eyes ranged over her.

'Why are you looking at me like that?' she demanded.

'Like what?'

'As if you're seeing me for the first time.'

'Maybe I am. I was thinking of you having to cope with your mother's illness. I really am sorry you didn't know where to find me.'

'As I said before, it doesn't matter. Anyway, I'm used to coping. I've had to do rather a lot of it since my father died.'

'How do you manage for money?'

'Very well, thank you.' Her face flamed. 'I earn a good salary.'

'What about your father's pension? Doesn't your mother get that?'

'It goes to pay off his debts.'

'Surely the shop fetched something?'

'With a Homefare hypermarket a few miles away?

85

You must be joking!' Her hands clenched. 'When I think of what that company did to us—of all the other shopkeepers they've ruined——'

'Don't talk like a fool!'

'It's easy for you to say that.' She glanced at him. 'Homefare is a client of yours. They give you your living.' She dug her hand into the belt at her waist. 'How many little grocery shops will their new hypermarket at Watford put out of business? Or are you so busy looking for new sites for them that you've no time to care?'

'I'm not ashamed of my work,' he said evenly.

'You would be if you knew the people whose livelihood you were destroying.'

'What about the people Homefare are helping? We're a better-fed nation than we were fifteen years ago. If it weren't for supermarkets, food prices would be far higher than they are.'

Realising the futility of argument, she said nothing, and he straightened from the wall and came over to her. 'Let's talk about you and me instead.'

'I'm not in the mood for conversation.'

'Worrying about your mother won't help her. Come out for a cup of coffee.'

Not giving her a chance to refuse, he propelled her to the street. As always she felt small beside him, and since she was average height it was a pleasant feeling. But then it was always pleasant to be with this unpredictable man who came in and out of her life so erratically.

'Don't you ever make a proper date with anyone?' she asked as they walked in the direction of Wigmore Street. 'Every time you've taken me out it's always been on the offchance.'

'Do you want a gilded invitation?'

'You know what I mean. Like tonight, for instance. You decided you wanted to see me, so you went to the office; but when you left me last night you said nothing about seeing me again.'

'Do I need to state the obvious?'

'It isn't obvious to me.'

'It should be.' He put his arm around her waist and pulled her closer to his side. 'I thought you knew I want to see you every minute I can.'

'I'm not a mind-reader,' she retorted.

'I was hoping you were a lip-reader.' There was laughter in his voice. 'Didn't the way I kissed you last night tell you anything?'

'Only that you're an expert in making love.'

'You don't know the half of it!'

Nor do I intend to, she decided. She was already thinking far too much of Red Clark, and had a strange presentiment that if she allowed herself to go on thinking of him it would lead to heartache. She had never known anyone so difficult to analyse. It was almost as if he put an invisible barrier between himself and everyone else, a barrier of banter behind which the real man was hidden. Unless there was no real man. Was Red the sort of person who lived only for his work and regarded the women in his life as a hobby? Yet his treatment of her had been far too understanding to be described in this way.

'Where exactly do you work?' she asked suddenly.

'I move around the country.'

'What's the name of your firm?'

'Trollope & King.' He laughed as he saw her disbelief. 'They really are called that.' He guided her into the mellow lights of a crowded coffee-shop and managed to find an unoccupied table. Amanda declined anything to eat, saying she had already had dinner.

'You couldn't have got all that much at the nursing-home.'

'I went out.'

'With the gentleman friend?'

'Must you use that term? It sounds like the servant-girl and the master!'

'I didn't want to call him your boy-friend in case it put ideas into your head!'

She could not help smiling, though at the same time she was aware of her reluctance to tell him about Clive. Just because he was the head of Brands there was no reason for her to feel guilty. She was only a minute cog at Homefare and she owed no allegiance to the company outside of working hours. Yet to admit that the man who wanted to marry her was the owner of a rival group was certain to cause acid comment.

'Don't look so worried.' Red broke into her thoughts, though his next words showed he had mis-read them: 'I'm sure your mother will be fine.'

Amanda concentrated on her coffee cup. 'I hope so.' She searched for something to say, reluctant to remain on the frightening topic of her mother's illness, but equally reluctant to leave the conversation open in case he reverted to the topic of her unknown boy-friend. Desperately she said the first thing that came into her head.

'Is finding sites for Homefare the only thing you do?'

'It's one of the most important.'

'Does your firm work for them exclusively?'

'Yes.' He raised an eyebrow, and she noticed it was a much darker red than his hair. 'You seem surprised by that.'

'I am. Why work for one group when you could sell the sites to the highest bidder?'

There was a gleam in the bright blue eyes. 'Are you suggesting I take the next site I find to Sainsbury's or Brands?'

'I wasn't suggesting anything,' she said hastily. 'I was merely curious to know why you didn't.'

'Because Homefare,' he said dramatically, 'has my total loyalty!'

'Be serious.'

'I am being serious, Amanda. They do have my loyalty.'

'Do you know Charles Foster?' she asked suddenly.

'What brought that up?'

'I wondered if that was the reason for your commitment to them.'

Red looked pensive. 'Could be. I never thought of it before. He's an amazing chap, you know: intelligent, handsome, fantastically rich.'

'A paragon,' she said coldly.

'I'll introduce you if you like.'

'Save yourself the bother. He's the last man in the world I want to meet. I hate everything he stands for.'

'He's no worse than any other supermarket boss.'

'At least Brands have integrity,' she said before she could stop herself.

'Then why didn't you stay on with them?' he said angrily.

'I work to earn a living,' she reminded him, 'and Homefare pay me more.'

'They obviously haven't bought your goodwill. That still belongs to their rivals.'

'I'm sure Homefare wouldn't care if they knew.

Anyway, they have *you* to defend them!'

She stifled a yawn, but it did not escape him, and picking up the bill he pushed back his chair. 'The day has worn you out. I'll take you home.'

'I'm staying at the Downshire.'

'By courtesy of the gentleman friend? He doesn't do things by halves—I'll say that for him!'

'He's very thoughtful,' Amanda said, and looked at Red with guileless eyes. 'I'm sure you would have done the same.'

'Not quite. I think you would be better off sleeping in your own bed. At the clinic you'll be on edge all night.'

'I'd be worse at home.'

'But at least you'd *feel* at home.'

It was an unexpected viewpoint, but she was too tired to consider it, and sensing this, he guided her out. The cool air momentarily revived her, but she was glad when they reached the Downshire again.

'I'll call you tomorrow, Amanda, to see how your mother is.'

'If she's a little better I must go to the office.'

'I'm sure Mr. Craig will understand if you don't. I'll have a word with him if you like.'

She shook her head, and Red kissed her lightly on the brow. 'I'll be working late tomorrow night, but I should be free around eight. If your mother's O.K., that is.'

'I'm afraid *I'm* not free,' she said stiffly, remembering Clive's kindness and feeling obligated to keep herself available for him.

'Some other time, then,' he said without any regret in his voice, and giving her a smile strode down the street.

She remained watching him. How casually he kept their relationship; kissing her with passion one moment and treating her as a platonic friend the next. And she still did not know where to contact him if she wanted to do so. He had promised to give her a telephone number, but he had forgotten. Or had he deliberately not wanted to remember? With a deep sigh she pushed open the door of the clinic and went inside.

CHAPTER SIX

MRS. STEWART was a little better in the morning and Amanda went to the office knowing she would worry less if her mind was kept busy. Clive had telephoned her while she was having breakfast and, delighted at her news, arranged to see her that evening at the Savoy.

'I'm not sure what time I'll be free,' she said. 'I have yesterday's work to catch up on as well as today's, and I also want to go back and see my mother.'

'Don't worry if you keep me waiting. I can always have a drink in the bar.'

As she had expected, there was a great deal of work to do in the office, though Mr. Craig insisted she take extra time during the lunch-hour to return to the clinic.

'As a matter of fact I'm surprised you came in at all,' he vouchsafed. 'You look extremely tired.'

'I didn't sleep well,' she explained. 'I stayed at the Downshire last night and I kept waking up every time a nurse passed the door.'

'It would have been better to have gone home.'

'That's what Red said. Mr. Clark,' she added, seeing her employer's uncomprehension.

'I hadn't realised you were still seeing him.'

'Only from time to time,' she smiled. 'He's too erratic ever to make a proper date.'

Gordon Craig smiled. 'You should tell him.'

'I did, last night.'

Mr. Craig cleared his throat and, picking up a letter from the pile in front of him, began to dictate a reply. He continued steadily for an hour, and might have gone on longer had he not been interrupted by a telephone call that sent him hurrying from his office an hour before his usual lunch-time. He returned an hour later than usual too, his flushed face and benign manner making her wonder if he had been celebrating something. She was not left long in doubt, for hardly had he sat down when he told her that the company had acquired three more hypermarket sites.

'Counting Watford, it means we'll have four in the Home Counties. It's a great *coup* for Mr. Foster.'

'I don't see why. If you have the money to buy the land where's the problem?'

'You need more than the land, Miss Stewart. You need planning permission from the town council. And many councils won't give it to you because they're unwilling to have the shopping taken out of the town centre. Other shopkeepers object.'

Appreciating the reason, Amanda's curiosity was aroused. 'How did Mr. Foster get permission?'

A guarded look came over Mr. Craig's face, and some of his expansiveness evaporated. 'He has tenacity, Miss Stewart. Tenacity and ability.'

'The other day you said he was obstinate.'

'It's obstinacy if I don't agree with him, and tenacity if I do!'

The double-edged remark reminded Amanda of her ambivalent feelings towards Red. When they were together she enjoyed his teasing references to her beauty, and his casual yet warm behaviour which made her feel liked without feeling idolised. But away from him, she remembered only his unwillingness to be bowled over by her appearance and his habit of turning up to see her without making arrangements beforehand. No wonder she found Clive more satisfying. There was no doubt in her mind how *he* felt about her. If he could become a little more spontaneous, and Red a little less so, they would both be ideal. She frowned, annoyed at where her thoughts had taken her. It did not matter to her if Red was ideal or not. Clive was the man who counted; Clive, who had asked her to marry him.

'I'll be leaving the office early,' Mr. Craig interrupted her reverie, 'so you might as well go off too. I expect you're anxious to see your mother.'

'I saw her at lunch-time,' Amanda said. 'I'm going out to dinner before I go back to the clinic.'

'A good idea. Is it with Mr. Clark?'

'No.'

'Never mind, there are plenty of other nights.'

Amanda wondered if this were true. If she agreed to marry Clive there would be no other men in her life. Indeed if she were honest about the situation there would be no other men now. Yet she was still too unsure of her feelings towards Clive to allow him to monopolise her time exclusively. Backwards and forwards her thoughts went. One moment she believed she was doing the right thing, the next, she felt she was being unfair both to Clive and Red. Not that Red gave the impression of caring whether or not she went out with anyone else. His teasing references to her gentleman friend gave no indication of real jealousy. Which was just as well, of course. Anyone as casual in their relationships as he was had no right to dictate the terms of it.

It was well before eight o'clock when she reached the Savoy. Good news of her mother's progress—she had spoken to the doctor before leaving the office— gave buoyancy to her step and a sparkle to her appearance which drew several admiring glances, and because she felt unexpectedly happy she responded to them and even went so far as to wink provocatively at one man old enough to be her grandfather. Some of her mood evaporated when she entered the bar and did not find Clive. For several moments she hesitated by the entrance, then realising he must have taken her at her word and decided not to come here until after eight, she went back into the foyer and hovered by the bookstall which, though closed, still displayed several jacketed books for her to look at.

The prolonged stare of a young man in a sharply cut suit decided her against remaining where she was, and buttoning her brocade coat up to her throat, she went out of the hotel.

Slowly she wandered along the Strand in the direction of Charing Cross. The wind was unexpectedly cold and a fine drizzle sent her scurrying back towards the hotel. As she reached the narrow turning that led to the main entrance, a chauffeur-driven Rolls-Royce swept past her. Stepping back to avoid being splashed by the wheels, she saw Clive in the back. But it was the man who sat beside him who commanded her attention. A man who had said he did not know Clive Brand; who barely twelve hours ago had said he worked exclusively for Homefare.

If that were true, why was Red with Clive now?

Keeping to the shadows, she moved closer to the entrance. The Rolls stopped and the two men got out.

'This discussion has been extremely interesting,' she heard Clive say. 'I'll think over what you've said and be in touch with you.'

Red gave one of his inimitable shrugs, but his reply was spoken too softly for her to hear, though she clearly saw the handshake that passed between the two men before he jumped into a taxi that had just deposited a fare. As the cab swung in her direction, Amanda turned her back on it, remaining motionless until it swung into the Strand. Only then did she enter the hotel.

Clive was already seated at a table when she reached the bar, and unusually conscious of him as he greeted her, she sensed an excited tension in him.

'Have you had a busy day?' she asked, when he had discussed and suitably commented on her mother's progress.

'No more so than usual,' he replied.

'I arrived earlier than I anticipated,' she said casually, 'but you weren't here.'

'I had an unexpected meeting.' A waiter paused at their table and he ordered the drinks. 'You look very beautiful tonight,' he said when they were alone again.

Impatient to return to the subject which was uppermost in her mind, Amanda asked: 'Was it an important meeting?'

'I'm not sure. It might be.'

'That's a funny answer. Why aren't you sure?'

For an instant Clive was motionless, then his hand came up to touch the grey at his temples, a gesture he often did when he was searching for words.

'It's unlike you to be curious, Amanda.'

'I thought you'd be pleased that I am taking an interest in your affairs.'

It was the right thing to say, for he immediately relaxed.

'My meeting was concerned with buying and selling.'

'I didn't think it had to do with knitting!'

He chuckled and shook his head. 'I can't tell you any more than that, my dear.'

Drinks were set before them, and as the waiter moved away, Amanda spoke again. 'Don't you trust me, Clive?'

'It isn't a question of trust, my dear. My meeting tonight was a confidential one—not just for me but for the other person. If it were not for that, I *would* tell you.'

'You mean the man you were with doesn't want anyone to know you were together?' Amanda asked, before she could stop herself.

'What makes you think it was a man?' Clive countered.

'I'd be furious if it were a woman.' She was delighted at her quick response, and Clive, flattered by it, laughed and toasted her with his glass.

'It *was* a man,' he admitted, 'and he would be very annoyed if our meeting was found out.'

The words ended any lingering hope that Red was innocent. Despite last night's avowal that he worked only for Homefare, he was obviously offering his services to the highest bidder. Yet how amused he had pretended to be when she herself had suggested he do this. 'Homefare has my total loyalty,' he had said, and like a fool she had believed him.

The depression that engulfed her was so deep that she marvelled afterwards how she had managed to get through the evening without Clive becoming aware of it; but then Clive frequently failed to understand her moods. As long as she looked beautiful and smiled at the right time, he was content to do all of the talking.

Tonight he was full of his impending trip to Canada, apologising for its unexpectedness and assuring her he would be back within a week.

'I hope my mother's home by then,' she said as they drove back to the flat.

'I don't want you rushing her out of the nursing home,' he warned. 'She must stay there until the specialist says she can go.'

'But the expense is——'

'My worry,' he interrupted.

'It's my worry too. I can't take so much money from you.'

'You won't take anything else,' he said bitterly.

'But I'll never be able to repay you.'

'Being my wife is all the payment I need.' He took one hand from the wheel and caught hers. 'Think of our future while I'm away, Amanda. We would have a wonderful life together. You would have everything you wanted.'

'You sound like Aladdin's lamp!'

'Then why not rub me?'

It was a surprisingly humorous remark—for he was not given to making them—and she burst out laughing. But there was no echoing laughter from him, and as he stopped the car outside the flat he gripped her shoulders and drew her close.

'I meant what I said, Amanda. I want to give you everything: clothes, jewels, furs. I want the world to see how beautiful you are. Will you promise to think about it while I'm away?' She nodded, and he stroked her long, red-gold hair. 'I'd like to twine each strand with diamonds,' he said softly. 'You're so beautiful, so beautiful.'

He kissed her lightly, then as he felt her lips tentatively move beneath his, his arms tightened and his kiss deepened. His mouth became fiercer. She felt the salt taste of blood and gave a little moan. Instantly he let her go.

'I'm sorry, darling,' he said jerkily, 'you make a man lose control.'

It was a thought that frightened her when she thought about it later. Tonight she had been able to escape the hard pressure of Clive's kisses, but what would happen if she were his wife? Would his passion, once assuaged, be less demandingly cruel, or was he the kind of lover who enjoyed using his strength to conquer and hurt? Repelled by the thought, she sat up and switched on the light. The glow of the lamp did not dispel the gloom that still pervaded her, and slipping on a dressing-gown she went to the kitchen to heat herself some milk.

Returning to the bedroom with it she saw her reflection in the mirror, pale and slim as a white candle, with her hair a glowing flame on top. *Radish-head*. The words came into her mind, bringing with them a picture of Red that sent her trembling. She tried to push the thought of him away, but he would not go, and she sat on the bed and once again went over all that Clive had told her about his meeting tonight. Why hadn't she admitted that she had seen him and Red

98

get out of the car? That she knew exactly who Red Clark was and for whom he worked? Had she done so, Clive would immediately have guessed that she knew the reason for their meeting. Her hands shook and some of the milk spilt on the coverlet. She set the glass on the bedside table and, too restless to sit still, paced the room. Were all business men so ambitious that they would stop at nothing to get what they wanted? Yet if Clive was guilty of behaving badly, Red was doubly so. It was understandable for Clive to try to do all he could to get better sites than his competitors, and even to put in a counter-bid for sites that Homefare were already trying to buy. This might not be commendable tactics, but it was accepted as the norm. What was not accepted was for an employee to sell his company's secrets and plans to a rival one.

Yet she was guilty of the same behaviour. Though she worked for Homefare, she had agreed to spy for Clive. Regardless of what justification she thought she had, she was no better than Red. Yet knowledge of her own guilt did not lessen her scorn for what Red was doing, the more so because she had believed in his integrity; had seen, in his carefree manner and frank good humour, a disregard for the fleshpots.

It was a relief to go to the office the next morning, though she nervously anticipated a call from Red and wondered if her feelings would show in her voice. He had not telephoned her yesterday to ask about her mother, and when five-thirty came without word from him, she was both relieved and hurt. He was more than unpredictable and disloyal: he was uncaring. Her longing to see Clive, to be close to someone who was reliable and demonstrably affectionate, was so strong that had it been possible she would have rushed into

99

his arms and agreed to marry him. But he was already winging his way across the Atlantic, and instead she hurried to the clinic, making an effort to look cheerful as she entered her mother's room.

Mrs. Stewart was sitting up in bed, self-conscious in a silk bedjacket trimmed with osprey.

'Madame Pompadour, I assume?' Amanda quipped.

'I feel like it,' her mother confessed. 'Your young man is most unexpected—and delightful—in his choice of gifts. Look around.'

Amanda did so. The bouquet which Clive had sent yesterday had been removed from the dressing-table and put on the window ledge, and in its place stood a miniature colour television set, its very smallness signifying its large price. Beside it were a dozen of the latest books and a flagon of French scent.

'The television gives a perfect picture,' Mrs. Stewart said. 'I was watching it all the afternoon. It's much better than flowers or grapes. I just feel guilty because it's so expensive.'

'He can afford it,' said Amanda. She would be reluctant to accept expensive gifts for herself, but she felt no guilt at letting her mother do so. How wonderfully kind Clive was; amazingly daring in his choice of gifts too, she thought, looking again at the fetching bedjacket. With osprey feathers the price they were, it must have cost him almost as much as the television set.

'Are you *sure* he can afford it?' her mother asked, still doubtful. 'He didn't strike me as being all that well off.'

'Don't be silly, darling. His car alone costs more than the price of an average house!'

'I would never have thought so. Still, I'm not much

of a judge of sports cars.'

'Sports car?' Amanda said faintly.

Only then did Mrs. Stewart realise they were talking at cross-purposes. 'It was Red who sent me these things, dear, not Mr. Brand.'

Amanda collapsed on to the nearest chair. Though Red might be a successful estate agent, the gifts he had sent her mother must have cost him much more than he could afford. Hard on this thought came the picture of him stepping out of Clive's car. Bitterness caught at her throat and she swallowed painfully. Selling Clive information about sites would enable him to buy far more than a television set. But it was impossible to say any of this to her mother, and she forced herself to talk of other things, inordinately relieved when a nurse came in with a supper tray.

'I didn't know you were here, Miss Stewart,' the girl said. 'Would you like me to bring you something to eat?'

'I'll go out for a snack, thank you. I can do with some fresh air.'

Promising her mother to return in time to have coffee with her, Amanda left the Downshire, resolutely refusing to acknowledge her disappointment that no red-haired man was waiting to greet her as she stepped into the street. Making her solitary way up Harley Street and into Wigmore Street, she searched for a restaurant. The one where she had had coffee with Red loomed invitingly in front of her, but she was unwilling to go there, and wandered along Marylebone Lane instead. She chose the first restaurant she saw, a small but expensive French one, where she ate pâté and fillet steak with a total lack of appetite. Only as she paid the bill and saw the high price did she think of

Clive and what marriage to him would mean for her. It was a pleasant thought, signifying not only financial ease for herself but for her mother too. Yet as she strolled back to the clinic she knew it was impossible for her to marry a man because she wanted security; she must be positive that she loved him too; that she would love him if he were a pauper. Was it foolish of her to be so unworldly? After all, she was extremely fond of Clive; surely that was enough upon which to build a marriage? She tried to envisage herself as his wife, but she could not do so. Unbidden, Red flashed into her mind: tall, laconic, with a glint of humour in his eyes and a sardonic tilt to his mouth. No, he was too detached and elusive to make anyone a good husband. He was an amusing escort and nothing more. Worse still, he was without integrity.

The small television screen was disseminating colourful news—literally and figuratively—when Amanda re-entered her mother's room. Silently she sat and watched the changing programmes, forcing herself to concentrate yet unable to take anything in. It was a relief when nine-thirty came and she could leave, though it was not until she reached the safety of her flat that she allowed herself to relax. It was then that depression engulfed her again, made even worse by the knowledge that she was very little better than the man she was judging. Though she had not yet given any of Homefare's secrets to Clive, she had promised to do so as soon as she could, and this promise made her no less despicable than Red.

CHAPTER SEVEN

SEVERAL days passed and Amanda did not hear either from Clive or Red. She could not help being wryly amused that both of the men in her life should have gone out of it at the same time. Not that Red had totally disappeared, for though he did not call her, he regularly telephoned the nursing-home to enquire about her mother's health. Perhaps he had grown tired of her, she mused, when the fifth day came and went without a word from him. He was good-looking enough not to be short of girl-friends.

Resolutely she concentrated on thoughts of Clive. Not that she could ever picture him as a boy-friend; the word evoked someone younger and gayer. Perhaps marriage would make him more light-hearted. Guiltily she pushed away the hope knowing it was unwise to expect marriage to change a person. One either accepted them as they were or one didn't marry them.

Clive was still very much in her mind when she left the nursing-home that night, and he came closer still when she met the specialist whom he had asked to look after her mother.

'My secretary has been trying to contact you this afternoon,' Sir Duncan Willis said.

'Is anything wrong?' Amanda asked nervously.

'Not at all. Your mother will be well enough to leave here at the end of the week. That's why I wanted to talk to you.'

'That's wonderful news!'

Sir Duncan smiled. 'I'm not keen on her remaining in London for the rest of the winter. Her chest is still weak and I would like her to spend a couple of months in a warmer climate.'

'We can't afford it, I'm afraid. In the normal course of events my mother wouldn't even have come here.'

'I realise that.' Sir Duncan hesitated, then said abruptly: 'Mr. Brand spoke to me about your mother before he went away. I told him what I've just told you, and he asked me to make any arrangements that were necessary.'

'What sort of arrangements?'

'For your mother to go to a nursing home in Tangier. It's run by nuns and I was able to recommend it personally.'

'It's out of the question,' Amanda said sharply. 'We can't afford it.'

'Mr. Brand is meeting all the expenses,' Sir Duncan said smoothly. 'I'm surprised he didn't tell you before he left.'

'He never said a word.'

'Some people find it difficult to talk of such things. He is a most generous man.'

'I know,' she said huskily, 'and it puts me under an awful obligation.'

'I'm sure that's the last thing in the world he would want. Your mother isn't the first person he has helped, you know.'

Amanda was astonished. Clive had been exceptionally generous, but his fastidious and phlegmatic personality did not conjure up a picture of someone who haphazardly bestowed largesse on the world.

'I'm referring in the main to his concern for his staff,' Sir Duncan went on. 'And if he's generous to those who work for him, you shouldn't be surprised if he's equally so with you.'

Amanda coloured and the consultant smiled. 'You would be wise to accept Mr. Brand's offer. Sunshine is what your mother needs.'

Unconsciously she glanced behind her to the window. Even in the darkness she could see the rain running down the pane. 'Wouldn't she be lonely in a foreign nursing home?'

'Most of the nuns speak English, and Tangier is very cosmopolitan. I'm sure your mother will soon find friends among the other patients.'

'There doesn't seem much for me to say, does there?'

'Only the word "yes".' He paused expectantly, and Amanda nodded. 'Good,' he said, moving to the door. 'I'll finalise the arrangements and your mother can leave on Saturday.'

'Will she be well enough to travel on her own?'

'It's a direct flight, and she'll be met at Tangier airport.'

To Amanda's consternation, her mother refused to accept Clive's latest generosity.

'I'm already too much in his debt, and if I go to Tangier for two months ... No, dear, I'm coming home.'

'Why spoil the ship for a ha'porth of tar?' Amanda asked.

'Being in a nursing home for two months will cost more than that,' Mrs. Stewart retorted. 'And the more we accept from Clive, the more obligated you'll feel towards him.'

'I won't agree to marry him from a sense of duty,' Amanda said more positively than she felt. 'I'm much more likely to marry him if you *won't* go to Tangier.'

'I don't know what——'

'If I'm actually his wife, you won't have any compunction in accepting his help! And if that's the only way I can get you to go abroad ...'

'You win,' Mrs. Stewart muttered. 'But I'm not happy about it.' She looked intently at her daughter's face. 'Don't you really know how you feel about Mr. Brand, or are you worried because he's so much older than you?'

'It has nothing to do with his age. I'm just not sure I love him enough.'

'Then go out with more men. You've been here night after night and it isn't good for you. You're young and lovely and——'

'Very tired,' Amanda intervened. 'I'm going home for an early night. I'll see you tomorrow.'

At home, she sat down to write to Clive. It was not an easy letter to compose, for she wanted to make it clear that even though she was accepting his help she was determined not to let it affect any decision she made regarding her future.

'It would be wrong for me to say I'll marry you out of gratitude. Such a marriage would be doomed to failure. Besides, you deserve to be loved for what you are—not what you have. That's why I want you to forgive me for still keeping you in suspense. I know it's hard for you, but if it's any consolation, it's equally difficult for me.'

By a strange coincidence her letter crossed with one of his, and the matter-of-fact account he gave her of his trip brought him so vividly to mind that she could picture him sitting at a desk writing it, his head tilted, a lamp picking out the grey at his temples.

'I find it unusually pleasant to be back in my hometown,' he wrote. 'Though I would be happier if you

106

were with me. The store I opened here three months ago is doing exceptional business and I'm planning several more. There is no shortage of space here—unlike England—and there are many other advantages. But more about that when I see you, which I hope will be next week.'

A strange reluctance prevented Amanda from taking Clive's letter with her when she went to the office. It was almost as if doing so was disloyal to Homefare. The idea was so ridiculous that it remained with her as she strap-hanged on the crowded subway train, and then fought her way through the heaving mass of people into the grimy air of Liverpool Street. But once inside the Homefare building the air was conditioned and germ-free, with draughts excluded by double glazing and ionizers maintaining the atmosphere at its most beneficial level of ozone. There was no doubt Charles Foster did his employees well. He might be a go-getter in business, but he was equally go-ahead regarding the welfare of his staff.

As usual Mr. Craig was in his office, deep in conversation with Saul Grock, head of Dairy Products.

'We can save ten per cent by buying Polish,' Mr. Grock insisted. 'Give me one good reason why I should turn it down.'

'Mr. Foster is the reason,' Mr. Craig replied. 'You know how he feels about the Danes—and the Dutch too. He'll give their products preference over everyone else.'

'Just because his father fought with the Dutch resistance!' Mr. Grock threw up his hands. 'At least let him sample the Polish. *Please*.'

'Very well. Get some of the sausage sliced—thin, mind you—and send it to his office.'

Not until Mr. Grock had gone did Amanda take in the morning post to her employer, and she stared with interest at the various cellophane-wrapped packages of bacon and sausages on his desk. 'Does Mr. Foster concern himself with every part of the business?' she asked.

'Indeed he does.'

'When does he find the time?'

'He has phenomenal energy. He finds time for everything.'

'I'd like to meet him. Does he ever come to head office?'

'Occasionally, but he's mostly in his own office at Park Lane—when he isn't travelling up and down England.'

'Looking for sites?' she questioned, and thought immediately of a wide-shouldered figure with flame-coloured hair. 'I suppose he sees quite a bit of Red Clark?'

Mr. Craig's look was difficult to fathom, but Amanda had the impression she had overstepped the mark, and she hastily proffered the letters she was holding.

'There'll be a lot of work for us to get out next week,' he said when they were sipping their mid-morning coffee. 'I hope you will be free to do some overtime?'

'Of course. I haven't worked late since I've been here.'

'Mr. Foster's a great believer in things being done during office hours. Not that he sticks to that rule himself. He works non-stop.'

'He'll die of heart failure.'

'I doubt it. He enjoys what he does; that's his great strength.'

'What's happening next week?' Amanda asked, bringing the conversation back to where it had begun.

'I have to prepare a report on the new hypermarkets. I should have all the data in by the weekend.'

'Don't the stores roughly cost the same?'

Mr. Craig laughed. 'Each piece of land we buy has a different price, and one store can cost twice as much as another. It's my job to work out the economics of each one.'

'Have you ever been wrong?'

'I'm still here,' came the succinct reply. 'That should answer your question!'

The words conjured up a terrifying picture of the financial rat-race, with Charles Foster as King Rat. This fantasy remained with her throughout the day, occasionally interspersed with thoughts of Red, who worked for this superhuman being and who was currently double-crossing him too. It was now well over eight days since he had been in touch with her, though he still made regular calls to the nursing home. If he had found another girl, surely he would stop enquiring about her mother? Perhaps it was pressure of work that was preventing him from getting in touch with her? If it was his job to find sites for new Homefare supermarkets, then Mr. Craig's reference to the great amount of work he had to do next week could well be the reason for Red's preoccupation. It was more pleasant to think this than to think of him wining and dining someone else, and for a reason which she refused to analyse, it made her feel considerably happier.

She was still feeling happy when she left the office, and she felt no surprise when Red loomed up in front of her, more handsome than she remembered, but just as casually dressed; this time in leather jeans and jacket.

'Don't you ever wear a suit?' she asked.

'That's a nice greeting for a long-lost lover!'

'Since you're neither lost nor my lover ...'

'I can soon remedy that!'

Hastily she began to walk, and he put his hand beneath her elbow and guided her to his car.

'Chinese or Jewish?' he asked. 'Or how about Indian?'

'I'll stick to convalescent! I'm expected at the nursing home.'

'No, you're not. I called in to see your mother and told her I'm taking you out.'

'You haven't changed a bit, have you?'

'Would you like me to?'

She shrugged, and flinging her an amused look, he set the car in motion. She had not told him where she wanted to go, and typically he did not ask her again but made the choice himself, ending up in the red and gold interior of a Peking-style restaurant.

As always, he knew his way around the menu, and ordered fast and fluently, pausing only to ask if she had any particular preference.

'I'll leave you to make the decisions,' she murmured. 'You always do!'

His eyes narrowed, and unexpectedly his lazy manner was replaced by concern. 'Does that mean you find me too bossy?'

'Most women like to be ordered around,' she replied, 'but only from time to time. You do it non-stop.'

'Because I think I know what's best for you.'

'I'm not an idiot!'

'Darling, I know that. You're a bright and intelligent girl—as well as being an exceptionally beautiful

110

one. If I seem to take command of you it's because——'
He stopped as the wine waiter approached them. 'Let's leave the rest of this discussion till we're alone. It'll be less wearing on my libido if we concentrate on chop suey!'

Throughout the meal he talked amusingly of what he had done during his absence, and she had the impression he had travelled a great deal, as well as spent many hours in tedious discussion with bureaucrats.

'It's part of the job,' he shrugged, when she made this comment. 'It's a foolish man who thinks he can ignore town councillors and planning officers.'

'I gather you were very successful,' she said and, aware of his keen glance, added: 'Mr. Craig told me three more sites were ready to be recommended to the Board. I assumed it was a result of your work.'

'You assumed right.' Red's voice was laconic, though his expression was not, and it prompted her next question.

'Were you with Mr. Foster this week?'

'Why do you ask?'

'Mr. Craig said he had been out of town looking at sites, and as you were doing the same thing ...'

'Yes, we were together,' he said lightly.

'Then you must know him quite well.'

'I do.'

'Why don't you ever talk about him, then?'

'What's the point? You made it very clear what you think of him.'

She could not deny this and glanced down at the hot slices of toffee-covered apple which had been set in front of her. The question which had been uppermost in her mind for the last fortnight was the one she had not yet asked, and she knew she would not

111

have any peace until she did. But how best to phrase it without letting him know she already knew the answer?

She was unaware that her anxiety was showing until Red reached out and covered her hand.

'What's bothering you, honey? You look like a girl with a big problem.'

'I was wondering about *your* problems,' she lied. 'If I were in your position I wouldn't work for one firm only. After all, *you* find the sites. You're entitled to offer them to the highest bidder.'

'I can't do that. My company belong to Homefare.'

'Then leave them and set up on your own.'

He shook his head. 'I have a watertight contract. Anyway, I seem to remember having this conversation with you before. And I told you then that I like working for Homefare.'

'So you wouldn't work for someone like Brands?'

'Never.' He speared an apple slice and ate it. 'This is good.' He took another one. 'Eat up, Amanda, before I polish yours off too!'

She made an effort to do as he asked, but the food stuck in her throat and it was all she could do to swallow it. In her innermost heart she had known Red would not admit his culpability, yet now it had actually happened she felt she had lost a friend; as indeed she had, for it was impossible to feel the same way towards him. It was bad enough knowing he was playing a double game without hearing him repeat the lie that he had a loyalty to Homefare.

Red gave no sign of noticing her withdrawn attitude and continued to talk banteringly during the remainder of the evening, though he quickly agreed to take her home when she pleaded tiredness soon after ten o'clock.

112

'So your mother is going to Tangier tomorrow,' he commented as they drove through the lamplit streets. 'I suppose your gentleman friend is paying?'

'What makes you think we can't afford it ourselves?'

'A private nursing home amid the palms? Pull the other one, sweetheart!'

'My friend *is* doing it,' she confessed gruffly.

'Why didn't you ask *me* before accepting his offer?' There was unexpected venom in Red's voice.

'How could I have asked you? I still don't know where to contact you!'

'Oh, lord,' he groaned, 'I never did give you that phone number, did I?'

'No,' she said tightly, 'you didn't. Even if I had died I wouldn't have known where to get in touch with you!'

He stopped the car abruptly, and in the light of the dashboard she saw he was grinning.

'What's so funny?' she continued, her voice still shaking with anger.

'*You* are.' He pulled her close and rested his chin on her head. 'Darling Amanda, you wouldn't *need* to get in touch with me if you died!' He tilted up her chin and kissed the tip of her nose. 'I'd come after you,' he whispered. 'Whether you were up or down, I promise I would come after you!'

Foolish tears blurred her vision, but before she could speak, his mouth fastened upon hers. He held her with a tenderness he had not shown before, his lips as gentle as his hands that moved lightly over her shoulders and down her back.

'My lovely adorable radish-head,' he murmured. 'I love you more than I've ever loved anyone in my life.' His mouth still remained against hers, his breath stirring her skin as he spoke. 'I hope you're going to admit that you love me.'

Held close in his arms Amanda knew the reason for all the irrational changes of mood which had beset her in the last fortnight. There was no longer any need to wonder why she had alternated between delight and despair, elation and misery. No need now to wonder if she could ever love Clive enough to marry him, when every fibre of her being told her that the only man whose touch she wanted was here beside her.

But she could not say she loved him; not until he had the courage to tell her about his relationship with Clive.

'You're taking a long time to answer me,' he said huskily. 'I never suspected you of shyness.'

Slowly she extricated herself from his arms, wishing the car was bigger so that she could move further away from him. He was heartbreakingly close, his tousled hair a rich auburn in the light of the dashboard, the colour of his eyes invisible, yet the gleam in them obvious. 'It's no good, Red. I—I don't love you.'

'Of course you do.'

'I don't. We hardly know each other.'

'I fell in love with you at first sight.'

'You hid it very well.'

'I wouldn't admit it to myself,' he said candidly, 'but being away from you this fortnight told me what a fool I was.' He caught her hand, ignoring her effort to pull it free. 'Don't be scared of me, Amanda, I'll never do anything to hurt you. I know I haven't been very loverlike or attentive, but I have my reasons.'

Thinking of the tightrope he must be walking, she felt she understood those reasons very well. Again she knew an urge to tell him she had seen him with Clive, and again she resisted it. It was far better to let him believe she did not love him.

'I meant what I told you, Red. I don't love you.'

'You're lying. Your voice is saying one thing but your lips told me another. You do love me, Amanda.'

'I find you physically attractive. It's nothing more than that.'

'Of course it is. I saw the way your face lit up when you saw me tonight. Darn it, I'm not blind. I can tell when a girl wants me!,'

'Wanting someone has nothing to do with loving them!' Her voice cracked. 'Of course I want you. You're good-looking and—and sexually exciting. Most girls would want you. But that doesn't mean I want to marry you. I *don't*,' she reiterated. 'Never, never, never!'

'Why the vehemence?' He pulled her round to face him. 'Why are you fighting me, Amanda?'

The urge to tell him she loved him was stronger than it had ever been. Her bones seemed to melt at his touch and she longed to twine herself against him and place her mouth on his, to feel the warmth of his body, the heat of his desire. But surrender today would only bring sorrow tomorrow, and she fought against the weakness of her senses.

Behind him in the rain-washed street a gleaming Cadillac glided past, and the sight of it reminded her of Clive, whose money had helped to destroy the integrity of the man beside her.

'Why are you fighting me?' he demanded again. 'You love me, I know you do.'

'It isn't enough.' Her eyes followed the tail-lights of the Cadillac. 'I want money,' she said recklessly. 'Lots of money. Much more than I can get from you.'

The silence in the car was electric, as if the very air was charged.

'Money?' Red said incredulously.

'Why should that surprise you? I'm sick of scrimping and scrounging! The man who wants to—who wants to marry me is rich. He can give me everything I want.'

'Everything except love.'

'Love doesn't last as long as diamonds!'

'Don't talk like a tart!' He flung her away from him and banged his hand on the wheel. 'You don't mean what you're saying.'

'I do.' She drew upon reserves of strength she had not known she possessed. 'I thought that wanting money is something you would understand. After all, you would do anything to get it, wouldn't you?'

'Are you asking me or telling me?'

She did not answer, hoping that if she remained silent he would say what she wanted to hear. But he remained quiet, and still in silence he switched on the ignition and headed the car north.

'I don't suppose we'll meet again,' Amanda said composedly as they drew up outside the flat.

'I'm afraid we must. I told your mother I would take her to the airport.'

'I'll make some excuse for you.'

'Why?' His voice was cool. 'I won't fall apart at the seams each time I see you. I'm not the type.'

'I didn't think you were.'

'Then I'll pick you up on Saturday morning. I assume your mother will be coming home first?'

'For a couple of hours. But if you decide not to come, let me know.'

'I'll be here,' he said briefly.

Not waiting for her to reach the house, he drove away with a shriek of tyres that more clearly indicated his mood than his last words had done. No matter what he said, he was bitterly hurt. If only she had found the courage to be totally honest with him. But what good would it have done? If she had told him she had seen him with Clive, he would merely have found an excuse, or at best, promised not to see Clive again. But what credence could one put on a promise extracted in such circumstances? None at all, she knew, and for this reason alone, was heartbreakingly aware that she had done the only thing possible.

CHAPTER EIGHT

MRS. STEWART was so pleased to be home again that it was all Amanda could do to persuade her to leave that afternoon for Tangier. She might well have failed if Red had not arrived soon after lunch, complete with a spray of orchids.

'I think I'll stay here for a few days,' Mrs. Stewart told him in a shaky voice. 'I don't want to leave Amanda just yet.'

'You're not going to the moon,' Amanda said briskly. 'You can phone me when you feel homesick.'

'Why don't you go with your mother?' Red asked softly as Mrs. Stewart went to put the spray of orchids in water.

'Because I have a job and I can't afford to leave it.'

'Wouldn't the rich man pay?'

'Certainly,' she snapped, 'but I have no intention of asking him.'

117

'Would you take the money from me?'

'You must be joking!'

'You mean you *mind* where it comes from? I wouldn't have thought that mattered to a girl like you!'

Her cheeks flamed, and had it not been for her mother's return to the room, she would have slapped his face. 'You're the lowest person I've ever met,' she hissed.

'I'm only taking you at your own evaluation, or didn't you mean what you said in the car?'

She closed her eyes against the sight of him. How handsome he looked, his brown suede trousers and jacket fitting his tall frame like a glove, his blue sweater the exact colour of his eyes. It was a cashmere one, she noticed, and knew that though his clothes looked casual they were expensive. But then he was obviously receiving plenty of money from Clive.

'I meant every word I said last night,' she whispered softly, afraid her mother might hear. 'Money is as important to me as it is to you; and like you, I'll do anything to get it.'

'I don't understand what you're hinting.'

Ignoring him, she went over to her mother. 'We must leave, darling, or you'll miss the plane.'

'I'd like to have an umbrella,' Red said as Mrs. Stewart stood up.

'What for?' she asked tremulously.

'To cover me against your tears!'

Mrs. Stewart laughed, and Amanda marvelled at Red's understanding. But then he had a knack of getting around people, as she knew to her cost.

To her surprise he had not come in his usual sports car, and a small grey saloon was parked by the kerb. Small but expensive, she noted as she climbed into

118

the back so that her mother could take the more capacious front seat.

'I borrowed it from someone at the office,' Red said, reading her thoughts, and then sliding behind the wheel, conducted the rest of his conversation with Mrs. Stewart.

Sitting behind him, Amanda had a chance to watch him without being observed. His hair was long but carefully controlled, the dark red waves brushed firmly down, though a few ends curled around his ears. Seen in profile he looked more serious than she remembered, and there was a strength in his jaw which, until now, she had only seen as obstinacy. During one of their conversations he had admitted to being thirty, but he looked younger, and she wondered if this was due to his light-hearted approach to life. Somehow she was sure the light-heartedness was only a surface attitude. The lines across his forehead indicated concentration, while the fine lines around his eyes, which she had not noticed a fortnight ago, spoke of the hard work he had done during his absence.

As if aware she was watching him, he glanced round. 'Comfortable?'

She nodded and huddled back into the corner, not trusting herself to speak.

Arriving at the airport, Red conjured up a wheelchair and, despite Mrs. Stewart's protests, placed her in it and announced that he himself would wheel her to the aircraft.

'You have to walk nearly as far as you fly these days,' he explained, 'and I can't have you fainting on the floor and crushing my orchids!'

Mrs. Stewart's protests died beneath her laughter, and she settled in the chair and allowed herself to be wheeled to the departure lounge. To Amanda's dismay the flight had been delayed and they had half an hour to spare. It was impossible to make casual conversation with Red, and afraid to remain silent in case her mother suspected they had quarrelled, she pretended she had to go to the chemist's. She remained there as long as she decently could and finally returned with a large bottle of cologne.

Only as she saw her mother's grey head bent close to the red one, was it borne in on her that she had given her mother a golden opportunity to talk about her to Red. Angry for not having guessed this would happen, she dumped the cologne on her mother's lap and looked covertly at Red as she did so. But his expression gave nothing away, though the tell-tale pink on her mother's cheeks convinced Amanda that her fears were justified.

With relief she heard the departure of the Tangier plane announced over the tannoy, and a few moments later she left her mother in the capable hands of a steward and headed back for the exit.

'What's the rush?' Red asked, striding beside her. 'Do you have a date?'

'Yes,' she lied.

'I thought the rich man was in Canada?'

She quickened her pace. So her mother had told him of Clive, but had she mentioned Clive by name?

'Why didn't you tell me it was Brand?' Red's question gave Amanda the answer, and she slowed her pace and glanced at him. But there was no anger on his face, only curiosity.

'Would it have made any difference if you had known?'

'I would have realised I was wasting my time with

you.' The glass doors in front of them slid open at their approach, and they stepped outside the terminal building and headed towards the car park. 'One thing surprises me, though,' he went on, catching her arm to prevent her rushing precipitately in front of a car which she was too het up to see. 'If you're so determined to marry money, why haven't you accepted his proposal?'

'You mean there's something my mother *didn't* tell you!"

'I asked no questions,' he said mildly. 'Proud Mama vouchsafed it all. Though I'm not sure she wouldn't prefer to have *me* as a son-in-law.'

'She's rather in awe of Clive,' Amanda said coldly. 'He doesn't have your easy facility with people.'

'You can say that again!'

'You speak as if you know him.' She made the comment as artless as she could, and disappointment washed over her as he gave an indecipherable grunt and said:

'Let's say he's not my type.'

'He's more honourable.'

'Do you think I'm *dis*honourable?'

She turned her head away, and when he spoke again his voice was hard. 'I have far more honour than you, Amanda. If I had been in your position I would have stayed with Brands and not gone to work for a company I despised.'

'Clive wanted me to leave,' she said icily, 'and I took the best-paying job I could get.'

'Reporting back all Homefare secrets, no doubt.'

'How dare you!' Her arm came up swiftly, but not swiftly enough, for he caught it in mid-air and pulled it roughly down to her side.

'No, you don't!' he grated. 'And why so fine a temper, or was the remark too close for comfort?'

'I don't like my integrity being questioned,' she stormed, 'and you're the last person in the world to do so. I couldn't avoid seeing you today, but for heaven's sake keep out of my life in future.'

'Does seeing me worry you so much?'

'Yes.'

'Because you love me but won't marry me?'

The question shocked her into honesty. 'Yes. I do love you, but I'll never marry you. Never!'

They had reached the car, and he unlocked it and waited until they were sitting inside before he spoke again. 'Tell me, Amanda, would you marry me if I were rich?'

'It's an academic question.'

'Not necessarily. I may come into quite a bit of money and I was wondering if it would make any difference.'

She stared deliberately through the window. How dare he think he could buy her with his ill-gotten gains? Even in her bitterness she could not help a wry smile at the old-fashioned phraseology that had come into her mind. But then she was discovering she was an old-fashioned girl when it came to the question of loyalty.

'I could never marry you no matter how much money you had,' she told him.

'You said you loved me.'

'That doesn't mean I consider you good husband material.'

Red's fingers came round her neck like a vice and forced her to face him. 'Why haven't you accepted Brand? I asked you that question before, but you

122

didn't answer.'

'I'm playing hard to get,' she said, and awarded herself full marks for acting ability. 'A man like Clive doesn't appreciate something unless he has to fight for it.'

'You'll mean you'll get more out of him that way,' Red said viciously.

'Naturally.'

'And what will *he* get from you? A loyal little wife who will love him as long as the money lasts? Or will you play fast and loose once you've got his ring on your finger?'

'Do you want me to let you know if I do?'

'Sure,' he said agreeably, and dropped his hands away from her. 'If I'm too poor to be your husband I'll settle for being your lover!' with a vicious jerk he put the car into gear.

'Don't kill me before my marriage,' she said sharply, and knew a stab of satisfaction as she saw the colour come into his face.

The return drive to London was completed in total silence, and in silence Red deposited her at her front door and drove away.

As she let herself into the house Mrs. Chadwalla came into the hall. 'Your phone was ringing for a long time this afternoon, Amanda, and then half an hour ago it rang again.'

'I'll leave you a key to the flat,' Amanda replied. 'I've been meaning to do it before, but I keep forgetting.'

Above her head she heard the telephone ring again, and she raced up to answer it. It was Clive, his voice so near that it was hard to believe he was in Canada.

'I wanted to let you know I'll be back tomorrow,'

he told her. 'As it's Sunday I thought you might like to meet me at the airport.'

'I'd love to.' She tried to sound enthusiastic. 'Give me your flight number in case you're delayed.'

He did so. 'Phone my house and ask the chauffeur to pick you up.'

'Wouldn't you trust yourself to my driving?' she teased.

'Of course, if you'd like to bring the Rolls by yourself.'

'I'd be scared to drive a car like that.'

'I'll give you a Rolls of your own as soon as you say the word,' he said at once.

She made a joke of his remark, but when she replaced the receiver she knew it was going to be difficult to keep him waiting for his answer much longer. Besides, she had nothing to wait for. She was not likely to meet anyone else who would be eligible and kind.

Going into the bedroom, she started to undress and, standing in her tights, stared at her reflection. Even the dingy mirror could not dim a radiance which came partly from colouring, partly from vitality. Her quarrel with Red had left a sparkle in her eyes, and they gleamed like aquamarine in her creamy-skinned face. No wonder men desired her, she thought dispassionately, and cupped her breasts with her hands. Would she be able to surrender to Clive's lovemaking and, equally important, be able to respond to it? Her body trembled at the thoughts that came into her mind, but she forced herself to consider them. Though Clive was generally tentative in his caresses, the occasional roughness of his kisses told her he would not be the gentlest of lovers. But perhaps a demanding man was what she needed, someone who would possess her and give her

124

no time to think. . . . She turned from the mirror. To think of whom? All too clearly she knew the answer, and the pictures that came into her mind this time were far different ones. How ironic that Red, who behaved so casually, should prove himself to be so tender. Even at the height of his passion she had known no fear of him.

Resolutely she put on her nightdress and climbed into bed. In the darkness it was even more difficult to control her thoughts, and she forced herself to breathe slowly and deeply, trying to calm herself this way. Gradually the restlessness within her died and she relaxed, but it was an enforced relaxation and she knew Red still lurked in the recesses of her mind, ready to emerge and torment her the moment she lowered her guard.

Morning sunshine dispelled her fears, and she opened the window wide, shutting it quickly as she discovered that brightness did not signify warmth. It was December and the sunlight was deceptive. She thought of her mother more than a thousand miles away, and wished she could afford to fly out and make sure she was settled. If Red had made the arrangements she was sure he would have bought her a ticket too. Irritably she banged her breakfast cup on the table. Clive would have been more than willing for her to have gone out with her mother if she had just said the word. It was despicable of her to be so carping.

Determined to keep herself occupied until it was time to go to the airport and meet Clive, she vented her energies on cleaning the flat, vacuuming and dusting until she had exhausted herself.

A hot bath, followed by toast and coffee, soon revived her, and jaunty in a green tweed coat tightly belted at the waist, she waited by the window until she caught sight of the chauffeur-driven Rolls edging its way down the street.

She reached the airport as Clive's plane touched down, and she had to kick her heels for half an hour before he finally emerged through Customs. He looked as he always did: quiet and distinguished, giving the impression of slowness yet moving towards her with surprising speed. Disregarding the chauffeur, he kissed her fiercely.

'I missed you,' he said, drawing back but still holding her by the arms. 'You're more beautiful than ever.'

'In my old tweed coat?'

A look of irritation flashed across his face and she was annoyed with herself for forgetting that he hated her to be deprecating about herself. Quickly she began to walk with him towards the exit.

Soon they were speeding towards London, with Clive giving her a résumé of his trip. It had been a strenuous one for him, though he looked unusually alert and fresh.

'I always sleep when I'm flying,' he said as she remarked on it. 'Jet-lag is something that never bothers me.'

'You're lucky.'

He caught her hands. 'You could make me luckier still. Have you thought of me while I've been away?'

'I remembered you every time I went to the clinic and saw my mother. You've been so wonderful, Clive.'

'That wasn't what I meant. I don't want you to think of me because you're grateful, but because you missed me.'

'Of course I missed you.'

He drew her hand to his lips and then lowered it,

126

but he still kept hold of it even when they arrived at his house.

'It's good to be back,' he sighed, and looked with satisfaction at the flower-filled hall and the log fire burning in the drawing-room grate.

Amanda followed his gaze, but knew a strong desire to rumple the uncreased pillows on the sofa and to leave her shoes lying in the middle of the pastel carpet. To do anything in fact that would give the house a more lived-in air. Yet to say so would only elicit another demand from Clive that she make up her mind to marry him. How much longer could she prevaricate? The question drew her restlessly to the window, and she glared out at the small courtyard that gave on to the back of the house. Green-painted tubs filled with green bushes stood like sentinels on the flagstones, and four wrought-iron chairs were grouped around a table in the far corner.

'The garden seems to me waiting for you,' she smiled.

'I like it to look as though I could step outside and sit down in it.'

'You'd freeze to death if you did!'

'I've no intention of doing so. I just like it to *appear* ready.'

'There must be a deep psychological reason for that,' she joked.

'I suppose there must. I like everything to look as though it can be used immediately. You'll never see empty grates in this house, nor do I believe in keeping silver hidden in cupboards. Beautiful things are there to be seen and utilised—and that applies to a garden as well as to a woman.'

'Do women need to be used?'

'Not in those terms, my darling, but in order to be at her best, a woman must know she is loved and wanted; that her beauty is appreciated.'

'What about ugly women? They like to be wanted too.'

'I dislike ugliness in any form.'

'You can't deny that it exists,' she persisted.

'I'm not. I just don't want to be reminded of it.'

As always when he spoke in this vein she felt disquieted, and she was relieved when the butler came in with the tea.

Clive certainly did not believe in hiding his silver, she thought, as she looked at the magnificent tray and tea-set. There was even a silver kettle with a methylated lamp beneath it to keep the water hot. Buttered crumpets nestled in a silver salver and home-made jam glistened in a cut-glass bowl.

'I never knew you ate English teas,' she commented, pouring him a cup.

'At one time I had ambitions to be a country squire.'

'I can see you in a hacking-jacket,' she admitted. 'You would get on very well with the county types.'

He shrugged. 'No matter how hard I tried, I would always feel a foreigner. I can play an English squire in Canada and get away with it, but I wouldn't fool anybody if I tried to play the role here!'

She laughed. 'What other ambition has taken its place?'

'None. Business is my main interest. I want to make Brands the biggest supermarket group in the country. We're already the biggest in Canada.'

'Wasn't that enough for you?'

'I fancied trying my hand here.'

'Where will you go next?'

'I'm not going to expand any more. A lot of groups are thinking in terms of Europe, but that's not for me. I understand the mentality of my own countrymen and the English too, but I'd be lost among the Continentals.'

'Homefare are thinking of Europe.' She spoke without thought and was sorry the minute she had done so, for Clive stared at her.

'Which countries?' he asked.

'I—I'm not sure.'

'Why the hesitation? Or is it that you don't want to tell me?'

'I don't *know* what Homefare's plans are,' she said firmly, determined not to let him know she was lying. She could never betray the confidences she had learned from Mr. Craig, any more than she would betray any confidence she learned from Clive.

To her relief he accepted her answer at face value, and she relaxed again, though she knew with painful clarity that she would not be able to do so completely until she left Homefare. Indeed it was such an obvious solution that she was amazed she had not thought of it before. Besides, to stay there would only encourage her to continue thinking of Red.

'I'm going to change my job,' she said aloud.

'Don't change it,' Clive replied. 'Leave it and marry me.' He set his cup on the trolley and came to stand beside her. 'You won't regret it, Amanda, I'll worship you all my life.'

'Worship's an uncomfortable word, Clive. I want to be loved.'

'I do love you, how could you doubt it?' He sank down beside her and drew her into his arms. 'What can I do to make you say yes?'

'Nothing.'

'There must be something,' he said softly, and started to kiss her. 'Perhaps this will help you to decide.'

Without replying she closed her eyes and tried to give herself up to this moment, without thought of the past or future, but though she was able to keep her mind a blank, her body remained a blank too. She felt nothing as he continued to hold and caress her, and she made herself simulate some response. She must have been successful in doing so, for when he finally drew away from her there was a contented look on his face.

'You're just scared of getting married,' he said quietly. 'I haven't taken into account that you're so young.'

'Twenty-one isn't young.'

'It is to me.' He leaned back on the settee and lit a small cigar, taking it from an elegant crocodile case in his pocket.

'That's the first time I've seen you smoke a cigar,' she said. 'Now you really look like a tycoon getting ready for a take-over.'

He shot her a sharp glance. 'Who's been talking to you about take-overs?'

'No one. I said it because it went with your image.'

'You mean you haven't heard it at Homefare?'

'Why should I have?' She was puzzled. 'I don't understand you.'

He looked at the tip of his cigar. 'There have been a lot of rumours in the Press about my bidding for another supermarket group.'

'You wouldn't buy Homefare?' she asked, surprised.

'There's no reason why I shouldn't—if they were

willing to sell. Do you think they might?'

'How would I know? I'm just a secretary there.'

'But secretary to Gordon Craig. That's quite different.'

'He's never even mentioned the word take-over.'

Clive blew out a cloud of smoke. It softened his features, blurring the sharp line of his nose and chin. 'I'm still interested in knowing where they're planning their hypermarkets. I was hoping you might have found out something while I was away.'

She had been anticipating the remark, but could not stop her pulses beating fast now that it had come. 'I haven't found out a thing. No one talks about it.'

'I know they have several in the planning stage. That much I've managed to find out for myself.'

From Red, she thought miserably, but aloud said: 'Then you won't need my help, I'm sure your source of information is more knowledgeable than I am.'

'What's the matter with you, Amanda? You're shaking.'

'Only from relief. I haven't enjoyed being your spy.'

'My spy?' He was incredulous. 'You're not spying.'

'What else would you call it? You want confidential information about Homefare and——'

'They're trying to find out the same facts about me,' he interrupted. 'It's normal business practice.'

'Then you can keep it!'

'Darling!' he protested. 'I didn't *ask* you to work for them. You took the job yourself and you agreed to tell me whatever you could.'

'Because you made it seem like an obligation.'

He pounced on the word as if he had been waiting for it. 'Exactly,' he said quietly.

'If you're referring to what you've done for my

mother....' Tears choked her and she could not continue, indeed she had no chance, for he pulled her into his arms.

'I helped your mother because I *wanted* to, not because it put you under an obligation to me.'

'You just said I *should* feel under an obligation,' she accused.

'I didn't mean it that way. What I meant was that if I were in your place I would do everything in my power to help you.'

She gave a deep sigh. Clive had epitomised the difference between them and there was nothing she could say to make him understand her point of view. He had the blinkered eyes of a man who saw business as the be-all and end-all of his existence; who saw nothing wrong in using all methods, fair or foul, to make that business succeed. No matter his assertion that she owed him nothing for the money he had expended on her mother, she knew that in his heart he felt she did owe him something. The knowledge filled her with despair, and had she been able to do so, she would then and there have repaid every penny he had expended. But a wish could not be translated into a reality, and she was still left with her deep indebtedness to him.

'Don't look so distressed, Amanda,' Clive pleaded. 'If you feel so strongly about your duty to Homefare, then forget what I said. Having you love me is more important than knowing the whereabouts of a few stores.'

She rested her head against his shoulder. Only rarely did she make a spontaneous gesture towards him, and he murmured with pleasure as his hand came up and stroked her hair.

'I'm not a very grateful girl, am I?' she said huskily. 'You've done so much for me.'

'Any man in my position would have done the same. Your happiness means everything to me. If I could buy you the moon, I would.'

'I don't want the moon,' she whispered, but refused to admit what it was she did want. 'Please be patient a little longer, Clive. I'm sorry to keep you waiting.'

'It will all be worthwhile once you say yes.'

There was so much confidence in his words that she felt frightened by it, and was pleased when the butler, coming in for the tea-tray, caused Clive to move away from her. After this they sat side by side and watched the television until it was time for dinner. Then it was television again until she stood up to go at ten o'clock. She refused to let Clive drive her home and telephoned instead for a taxi.

'You've had a long day, Clive. I wouldn't dream of letting you take me home.'

'I wish you didn't have to go.'

Pretending she had not heard him, she slipped on her coat and went to the door, glad to see the taxi waiting at the kerb.

Alone in its draughty confines she knew that no matter how many times Clive said she did not owe him anything, she would always feel guilty unless she gave him all the information she could about Homefare. He had a greater right to her loyalty than the company who destroyed her father and hundreds of shopkeepers like him.

Though she did not love Clive as deeply as he loved her, she knew that eventually his persistence would wear her down and she would agree to marry him. Yet she would have to tell him she did not love him—that much she owed him—and if he decided he would not marry her.... But he would not do that. He wanted to possess her beauty; to clothe her and bejewel her; to have her by his side for everyone to admire. It was discomfiting to know that if she were not beautiful he would not want her; but then how many men would? Immediately she thought of Red, who had rarely commented on her appearance and found her beautiful in an old jumper and skirt. She clamped her lips tight, as though this could block him from her mind, but his image persisted, and she saw his mouth curved in its usual mocking smile, his eyes glinting with mischief.

She glanced through the window of the taxi and saw they had only a hundred yards to go. Rapping on the partition, she told the driver to stop.

'I need some fresh air,' she explained, and paying him, walked down the street, hoping that as the taxi turned and drove away, it would take with it all the unhappy thoughts that would not let her rest.

CHAPTER NINE

THE next morning Gordon Craig arrived at the office with his eyes streaming and a handkerchief to his nose. At mid-morning he looked considerably the worse for wear, and gratefully accepted the hot lemon and whisky which Amanda gave to him.

'I think I'll take myself home,' he sneezed. 'A day in bed should put me right.' He sneezed again. 'I'll have to tell Mr. Foster I won't be able to compute those figures he wants until the end of the week.'

'And maybe not even then,' Amanda interjected. 'I

doubt if you'll be back before next Monday.'

'I can't be away that long,' he protested. 'Mr. Foster has to have the figures by Friday, at the latest.'

'Would you like me to ring him and explain?'

Gordon Craig looked so horrified that Amanda smiled. 'He *is* human,' she said mildly. 'He can't blame you for getting the 'flu.'

'I'll call him myself. If you could close the door on your way out. . . .'

Amanda did so, and hardly had she settled herself before Gordon Craig left the office, promising to let her know when he would be returning. With her employer away ill, she suddenly realised she would not have any information to give to Clive, and she felt such an immeasurable sense of relief that she was almost light-headed; she could even think of Red without feeling depressed.

Though she had told Mr. Craig she had plenty of work to do, it was not enough to keep her fully occupied, and she spent part of the afternoon looking at the range of new samples which daily poured into head office. The majority of them would be discarded, either because they were unsuitable or too highly priced. If it was for the latter reason, the manufacturer was soon made aware that having his products in several hundred supermarkets was sufficient compensation for a lowering of his price. It was a tactic which rarely failed, and she had frequently watched Gordon Craig obtain a price concession that had staggered her.

That afternoon she saw Mr. Grock—for whom she was typing some letters—perform a similar job on the Betterporc representative. After an hour of tough discussion, during which the unhappy salesman was informed that Homefare might well look elsewhere for similar produce, the price was lowered by a penny per tin. A quick calculation of the thousands sold each week told Amanda it had been a good morning's work for the ebullient little buyer.

'Take home a few tins and try it for me,' Mr. Grock said, shovelling several of them across the desk.

'I don't like tinned sausages.'

'For the company you'll like 'em and eat 'em!'

'What happens if I don't like them—will you cancel the order?'

To her surprise he considered the question before shaking his head. 'I don't know your taste in food well enough. But I can tell you this: if my *wife* doesn't like them I'll cancel the order. I always say I married her because she's Mrs. Average Housewife!'

Amanda laughed. There was more kudos in working for Gordon Craig, but there was considerably more fun in working here.

The next couple of days passed quickly. As she had expected, Mr. Craig's doctor insisted he remain at home for the entire week, and once she had dealt with the post and filing each morning, there was little left for her to do. Because of this she spent her afternoons in Mr. Grock's office and, watching him work, remembered how eagerly she had wanted to be a buyer herself. But it was silly to think of such a thing now. If she married Clive she would be unable to work for anyone. Her time would be taken up in caring for him and running his various homes.

Somehow the thought did not seem as if it would be exciting or sufficiently absorbing. When children came along it would be much better. The thought of children was unnerving, making her realise the true intimacy of marriage. What would their children be like? she wondered. Quick-tempered like herself or as calm and determined as Clive? And what colour hair would they have? She had read somewhere that the genes of the more positive partner was likely to predominate. If that was the case, then the children would have dark hair. If she were married to Red neither of them would ever know who was the boss! She thought of rows of auburn-coloured heads ... carrot-tops ... radish-heads.... She banged her hands hard on the typewriter keys as though she were pummelling them on Red himself.

On Wednesday Clive took her out to dinner. Pressure of work had made it impossible for him to see her since Sunday, though he had called her each evening and sent her a bouquet of flowers. She was surprisingly glad to be beside him in the Rolls, and watched him weave his way competently through the traffic. Next to Clive she felt cosseted and cherished.

He took her to a restaurant bordering the Thames, where they dined at a window overlooking the water, with the lights of Battersea power station on the far side. Night lent the scene a strange enchantment and the few small boats shunting past brought with them the glamour of distant lands, though common sense told her they probably only came from Greenwich or further south along the river. It was not the sort of restaurant to which Clive usually took her. He preferred the more obvious glitter of the Savoy and Ritz, and it was only when their meal was served, and turned out to be excellent, that he lost his faint air of alarm.

'It's quite nice here, isn't it?' he said cautiously, looking round the dimly lighted room where even people at the next table were barely discernible.

'Though personally I like to see more of my surroundings.'

'You should be content just to see me,' she teased.

'I like other people to see you too.'

'You're a show-off.'

'Anyone lucky enough to show you off would be crazy not to do so.' He leaned across the table and caught her hand. 'We'll go to the Hilton next time.'

'You spoil me.'

'I'd like to do much more.' He squeezed her fingers. 'I thought we'd fly out to Tangier one week-end. We can stay there a bit longer if you like.'

'It would be super to go there for Christmas,' she admitted. 'It will be the first one my mother and I haven't spent together.'

'Then we'll certainly go there for it. That's a marvellous idea.'

She stared at her coffee cup. Christmas in Tangier with Clive. She would have to give him his answer then: either agree to become his wife or decide not to see him again. Yet how could she avoid seeing him when his money was buying back her mother's health? She sighed, wishing she could see money for the unimportant thing it was. Not that it was unimportant when you needed it; it was only when you had a great deal that you could afford to dismiss it—as Clive certainly could. The money he was expending on her mother meant nothing to him; she must remember this when it came to making her decision.

'Penny for your thoughts,' he said.

'They're worth more than that.'

'Several hundred pounds, no doubt.' His dark brows drew together. 'You're thinking of the cost of keeping your mother in Tangier.'

138

She nodded. 'I hate being in your debt.'

'The debt's in *your* mind, not in mine.'

It was pointless to argue and she searched for something else to talk about. But her mind was a blank and she pretended to watch the dancers whose outlines she could dimly discern in the Stygian gloom. Clive settled back in his chair, quietly smoking a cigar and content to watch her profile.

It was only as she turned to smile at him that she noticed the couple who had just come into the restaurant and were standing by the bar. Though the light was no brighter there than anywhere else in the room, a spotlight above the bar caught the man's hair, turning it to the colour of fire. Amanda's pulses leapt, and as she watched him he turned to his companion, his profile confirming her first astounded belief. Quickly Amanda moved her chair, determined to keep out of view, but she could still see Red clearly, as well as the girl with him, a ravishing blonde wearing more off than she was wearing on.

What unhappy fate had brought him here tonight? He had never taken *her* to an expensive place like this, yet the first time she came here with Clive, it was to find him here too. Anger and jealousy warred within her, but both gave way to the fear of what might happen if he saw her and came over to speak to her. Heaven knew what his malicious sense of humour might induce him to say, and how angry Clive would be if he discovered she had gone out with someone else on the nights he had supposed her to be at home. If only she had had the courage to tell him!

'Aren't you feeling well, darling?' Clive asked. 'You're very quiet.'

'I'm tired,' she said, and wondered wryly how many

times other women had used that lie as an excuse.

'I'll take you home.'

He signalled for the bill while Amanda's eyes flicked back to the bar. Red and the blonde girl came into the restaurant and were led to the opposite end of the room, where they disappeared into the darkest corner. Quickly she stood up, staying close to Clive as they went out.

'I had to park the car a few minutes' walk away,' he explained. 'Wait here till I get back.'

'Hoot for me. It'll save you getting out of the car again.'

With a smile he left her, and she went to the cloak-room for her coat. Her face was blanched of colour and it intensified the black of her velvet cloak. Hugging it around her, she returned to the foyer.

'When's the wedding, Amanda?' a sardonic voice asked, and she did not need to look to know who had asked the question. Bracing herself, she swung round.

Red was no less pale than she herself, but he looked astonishingly handsome in the sombre black of his dinner jacket. With her he had always been casually dressed, but for another girl.... The thought was so painful that tears pricked her eyes and she blinked rapidly.

'We haven't decided,' she said brightly, 'but I'll invite you to the wedding if you ever get around to telling me where I can contact you. Or do you always keep your girl-friends in ignorance of your address?'

'I live on a broomstick,' he grinned, 'like most warlocks!'

His humour was the last thing she could tolerate and it did nothing to appease her fury. 'If you followed me out here to be rude....'

'I followed you out to ask how your mother was.'

Amanda swallowed her anger. 'She's getting on very well, thank you. But now you're here, do stay and let me introduce you to Clive, or do you already know him?'

'I told you he's out of my league.' Red grinned so easily that if Amanda had not seen him with her own eyes get out of Clive's car, she would never have known he was lying.

'I'm sure he'd love to meet you,' she persisted.

'Another time.' He turned to go and without being able to stop herself, she called: 'Will I see you again?'

For several seconds he stared at her, then his face set into hard, unfamiliar lines. 'You were the one who told me to go,' he said coldly. 'And I still don't think I have enough money to meet your needs.'

Blindly she stumbled to the door and stepped out into the cold air. She had asked for that last hateful jibe and she had got it.

With each one of her nerve ends feeling exposed and raw, the last thing in the world Amanda wanted was a love-scene with Clive. But unaware of her turmoil and carried away by his own, he stepped inside the hallway when she opened the door of the house and was at the foot of the stairs when she stopped him.

'You can't come up at this time of night,' she whispered. 'The landlady wouldn't like it.'

'It's your flat.'

'It's not self-contained,' she said nervously. 'Mrs. Chadwalla wouldn't say anything, but—but I know she wouldn't approve.'

'I only want to kiss you,' he said.

His contrite apology shamed her, for she knew that had it been Red she would have made no protest.

'Dear Clive,' she whispered, and put her arms around his neck. 'You're far too nice for me.'

'Don't minimise yourself.' As always he could not bear her to be self-deprecating, and his momentary irritation took away the edge of his desire. Kissing her gently, he went out to the front step. 'Dinner at my house tomorrow,' he said. 'If you're determined to keep the wolf away from *your* door, then you'll have to come to mine!'

As it always did, his unexpected humour renewed her affection for him, and she stepped outside and kissed him again before saying goodnight.

Later, as she undressed, she wondered if marriage would help him unbend or whether she, instead, would grow more formal. At the moment she felt they were too different for their relationship to be continually harmonious. Yet with all the will in the world she could not envisage Clive becoming as light-hearted as Red. Nor would he be as dishonest. This last thought sent such a wave of despondency over her that she climbed miserably into bed and wished she had the vocation to be a nun.

Late on Thursday afternoon Amanda received a telephone call from Mr. Craig. His voice was still a croak, though he said he felt much better, and asked her to come to his home the following day to take some dictation.

'I want to complete those figures for Mr. Foster,' he explained. 'It's nonsense to let a bout of 'flu stop me.'

Promising to be at his home first thing in the morning, Amanda left the office early and, deciding not to bother to go home and change, set off for Clive's house.

Travelling in to the West End she was moving

against the mainstream of traffic, but when she reached Marble Arch she was in the thick of the rush-hour and, preferring a ten-minute walk in the cold and darkness to the stifling heat of a crowded bus, she set off along the Bayswater Road. Even walking she was besieged by noise and fumes, and she turned down one of the side streets to avoid some of it. The nearer she got to Clive's house the slower her steps became, and when she saw the red brick mansion ahead of her, she stopped completely and drew several deep breaths to try and compose herself.

It was ridiculous to feel like this. Clive was comparatively young, attractive and rich: a man whom the majority of girls would be delighted to consider as a husband. Yet here she was standing at the corner of the street wishing she need never see him again.

Bracing her shoulders, she moved to the front door. Simultaneously it opened and a tall figure was silhouetted against the light within. Recognition made her recoil into the shadows, afraid that she had been seen. But Red was talking too intently to Clive to notice anyone, and even as he ran down the steps his head was still turned in the direction of the broad-shouldered Canadian.

He had a different car at the kerb this time: a small grey Porsche which even Amanda, with her limited knowledge of cars, knew to have cost well over ten thousand pounds. He must have borrowed it from his office in order to make the right impression, she thought scornfully. Though if he went on the way he was going, he would no doubt soon be able to afford his own. With a rich, throaty purr the car shot away into the night, and as its tail lights disappeared, Amanda approached the house and rang the bell.

Clive came out from the drawing-room as the Spanish manservant let her in. 'Darling,' he said in surprise, 'you're nice and early.'

'I came straight from work. I didn't change; I hope you don't mind?'

'You look beautiful as always.' He led her to a settee and handed her a champagne cocktail. 'It's an excellent pick-me-up,' he explained, seeing her raised eyebrows.

'So is a strong cup of tea!'

'You're more of a champagne girl.'

Feeling at the moment far more like a hot milk and slippers one, she sipped her drink; bubbles effervesced beneath her nose and the glass was ice cold against her lips. A pity she didn't like champagne more; yet it would be ungracious to say so.

'Lovely,' she murmured. 'Thank you, Clive.'

Pleased, he sat down facing her. 'You won't be bored staying here to dinner?' he asked.

'I love the idea.' Her lashes veiled her eyes. 'Have you been home long?'

'Yes, I had a meeting here.'

'I know,' she said casually. 'I saw him leave. I know him, Clive. I met him when he came to Mr. Craig's office.'

Clive jerked forward, his face pale. 'For heaven's sake keep quiet about it; I don't want anyone to know.'

'I'm not likely to broadcast it.' She squared her shoulders. 'Aren't you ashamed?'

'What's there to be ashamed about?' His eyes narrowed. 'What we're doing is quite normal, you know. It often happens where two big companies are concerned.'

Since she had already had this argument with him,

she decided it was a waste of time to have another one.

'You can't convince me,' she said wearily. 'I just wish it wasn't with *him*. I suppose he'll make a lot of money out of it?' The words were forced from her.

'A great deal,' Clive echoed.

These words echoed in her mind for the rest of the evening, making it difficult for her to concentrate on anything Clive said. However, she must have behaved normally, for he did not notice anything amiss and, when the dinner was over, sat beside her on the settee and told her something of his earlier life and his first marriage. Only then was she able to pay more attention to him and look at him without seeing an image of Red.

'I'd like my friends and relatives to meet you,' Clive said. 'If we weren't going to Tangier for Christmas I'd suggest we went to Canada.'

Amanda had been dreading the thought of Tangier with Clive, but it was infinitely preferable to going with him to Canada. At least in Tangier she would be with her own mother, whereas to be with Clive's family —until she had finally made up her mind about him— smacked too much of hypocrisy.

'What are your favourite stones?' Clive asked, catching her hand and separating the fingers.

'I've never given it any thought.'

'Is it diamonds, or sapphires to match your eyes?'

'Soapstone!' she laughed.

'I'm being serious,' he said quietly. 'I want to buy you something special.'

'I'm sure I'll like whatever you buy—as long as it isn't expensive. I won't take an expensive present from you, Clive.'

'Price is relative.'

'It has to be relative to *me*.'

'Don't let's argue about something you haven't received yet! I'm sure we can find lots of other things to quarrel about.'

She shrugged and, wanting to change the topic, switched on the television set. What on earth had people used as an escape valve before this wonderful invention?

At eleven o'clock she stood up to go and Clive drew her into his arms.

'I feel so lonely when you leave me,' he whispered. 'If only I could dazzle you with my money!'

'Someone recently called me a gold-digger,' she said before she could stop herself.

'Then they don't know you very well. Next time anyone says that to you, refer them to me.'

She smiled and, excited by the curve of her mouth, he covered it with his own, kissing her with an intensity she could not match. She was aware of the heavy thudding of his heart and his quickened breathing, and knew an irrational longing to put the distance of the room between them. But when he finally released her she was careful not to move for fear of hurting him. But the effort of pretence made her nerves ragged, and when she was finally left alone in her flat, she sank down on the bed and wondered whether she would have the courage to live the rest of her life with him.

A restless night left her tired and dispirited, and she made up more heavily than usual, carefully rouging her cheeks and using a darker powder to lessen the pallor of her skin. Even her hair looked less vital and she pinned it away from her face. The style accentuated her delicate bone structure and made her look disarmingly young: like a little girl trying to be grown-up. Not that there was anything childlike about her figure. In a dark skirt and white frilly blouse she had a radiance that not even fatigue could diminish. Reflecting soberly that she was lucky in her genes, she set off for Mr. Craig's home.

It was typical of the man: a detached house in Wimbledon with a small, immaculate driveway and an au pair to open the door.

'Mr. Craig's expecting me,' she said.

The girl led her into a cheerful sitting-room. It was empty save for a wire-haired terrier who growled suspiciously and then retreated to the window. Gingerly Amanda sat down, wondering whether Mr. Craig would come in here to work or whether she would have to go upstairs. The door opened and she turned, the movement arrested as she looked at the man framed in the threshold.

'You!' she gasped. 'What are you doing here?'

Red scowled at her. 'I had some things to talk over with Mr. Craig. He tried to get you at home, but you'd already left.'

'I said I'd be here early.'

'You've had a wasted journey, I'm afraid. He isn't well enough to do any work.'

'But he asked me to come.'

'And I'm asking you to go.'

Her cheeks burned. 'I'd like to see Mr. Craig for myself, if you don't mind.'

'I'm not lying, Amanda. What reason would I have for sending you away?'

She frowned. 'Mr. Craig was most insistent about working with me. He has an important report to prepare and Mr. Foster will be furious if he doesn't get it.'

'Did Mr. Foster say so?'

'Of course not,' she said angrily, 'but Mr. Craig——'

'Has already spoken to Mr. Foster, who has ordered him to rest.' Red stepped forward and Amanda drew back, as though afraid he were going to touch her. Her withdrawal did not go unnoticed and his eyes glittered with anger. 'Mr. Craig's bedroom is facing you at the top of the stairs. If you think I'm lying, go up and ask him.'

Head high, Amanda walked into the hall and up the stairs, drawing a breath of relief as she opened and closed the bedroom door, blocking out those vivid blue eyes that threatened to bore into her back.

'Miss Stewart!' Mr. Craig, plump and pale in striped pyjamas, was sitting up in bed. 'I'm sorry you've had a wasted journey, but the doctor feels I shouldn't start work just yet.'

His voice was so hoarse that Amanda appreciated why the order had been given. 'I didn't mind the journey, Mr. Craig. I'm not all that busy at the office.' She paused. 'Would you like me to ring and explain to Mr. Foster that you're still not well?'

'That won't be necessary. He already knows.'

'Is there anything else I can do for you?'

'Nothing, thank you. Ring me first thing on Friday morning. If I feel up to it, I might do some work with you then.'

Downstairs in the hall again, she hesitated, not sure whether to go and inform the maid she was leaving. She listened but could hear no sound coming from anywhere, and deciding it might be embarrassing to open doors, she picked up her briefcase and went outside. It had started to rain and she pulled a face at the lowering skies, annoyed that she had not thought to bring an umbrella with her.

'Can I give you a lift?'

Red's voice close to her ear made her start violently, and she looked up to see him in step with her. 'No, thank you.'

'Don't be crazy,' he said briefly. 'You haven't got a raincoat and you'll be soaked to the skin. Get in.' Before she could refuse he pushed her unceremoniously into his car—still the Porsche, she noticed—and then took the driving seat.

'The partners in your office must be very rich,' she remarked as they pulled away from the kerb. 'You seem able to borrow extremely expensive cars from them.'

'How do you know it isn't mine?'

'Perhaps it is,' she retorted. 'I'm sure you have many ways of supplementing your income.'

'Still talking in riddles?'

The violent way he changed gear told her that her remarks had hit home, and she was fiercely pleased.

'Since you know exactly what I mean, you can hardly call it a riddle.' She drew a deep breath, then said : 'I saw Clive last night. I had dinner at his home.'

'Good for you. I hope you enjoyed yourself.'

'Is that all you can say?'

'What do you want me to say?'

'Anything!' she burst out. 'Anything at all.'

'I've nothing to add.' He shook his head and a thick lock tumbled over his forehead. The urge to put out her hand and touch it was so strong that she was frightened she would not be able to stop herself, and she drew as far back in her seat as she could get. She

149

forced her mind to focus on his duplicity, wondering if he would have something to say if she told him she had seen him leave Clive's house last night. Only the knowledge that it would lead to a futile and probably bitter quarrel, kept her silent.

'How's your mother?' Red asked, breaking into her thoughts.

'Getting on fine, thank you.'

'Good.'

Another mile went by and Amanda stared out at the passing scene. 'I'm going to Tangier with Clive for Christmas,' she said finally.

'That will be nice for you. It seems your future is all settled. What's lover-boy buying you for Christmas—a cash-register?'

'I'll give it to *you* if he does. I'm sure you'll be able to use it too!'

'I don't have your deep interest in money. I prefer to work for mine.'

'How dare you——'

'Not that you *won't* be working for yours,' he went on, heedless of her flaming face. 'I imagine Clive Brand will expect very special things from his wife.'

'What's that supposed to mean?' she choked.

He glanced at her, and seeing her expression, gave one of his inimitable grins. 'I wasn't thinking of sex,' he said candidly. 'Just that Brand's the sort of man who will turn you into a puppet and expect you to dance every time he pulls the strings.'

'They'll be strings of pearls,' she flashed back at him. 'So I won't mind dancing to them!'

He muttered under his breath and turned to face the road. Several more miles went by before he spoke.

'I can't understand you, Amanda. You really fooled

150

me. I thought I knew the sort of girl you were.'

'One can never be sure of people. I've found that out myself.'

'You talk as if someone has let you down.'

Longing to say, 'You did!' she averted her head. 'It isn't important,' she said huskily. 'I don't expect much from people any more.'

'Don't become too cynical, Amanda. Believing in the basic goodness of people was one of your nicest characteristics.'

'I didn't think you thought I had any.'

'Come, come, you know very well that isn't true. I took you out often enough, didn't I? And it wasn't only on account of those big blue eyes. Still,' he continued, his smile bantering, 'there are lots of other lovely eyes around.'

'I'm glad to know you're so resilient.'

'I never did believe there was only one fish in the sea.'

'What have you caught yourself this time?'

'Not another red snapper! My new fish is a little blonde.'

'So I saw.'

'Of course, I was forgetting we met the other night.'

Temper brought tears to her eyes and she blinked them away. 'Where are *you* going for Christmas?'

The question took him unawares, for he answered automatically: 'New York,' and then clamped his mouth shut as though he regretted his reply.

'You *are* living it up,' she commented. 'Come into any money lately?'

'Not enough to satisfy *your* greed.'

Again he changed gear with unexpected viciousness, and accepting the futility of further conversation with him, Amanda buried her chin in the collar of her coat. It was hard to believe she was sitting so close to the only man she had ever loved, and yet at the same time be unable to communicate her love to him. If only she could make him see that what he was doing was wrong! Before she could stop herself she put her hand on his arm, and felt it tense beneath hers.

'Why do you always harp on *my* attitude to money?' she asked. 'What about yours? Haven't you done things for gain?'

'I don't see what one thing has to do with the other. If you'd care to explain. . . .'

'You know without my having to tell you.'

'I hate women who make a statement and then refuse to explain it!' He was angrier than he had been throughout the entire journey. 'If there's something on your mind, for heaven's sake tell me—or be quiet about it.'

She dropped her hand from his arm and said nothing. She had given him a chance and he had refused to take it; refused even to admit he understood what she meant. To explain herself would lead nowhere.

'I've nothing to say about the subject,' she whispered.

Once more they drove in silence. Amanda closed her eyes and pretended to doze, only opening them as the Porsche stopped outside the rear entrance to the Homefare building.

'Forgive me for not taking you round the front,' he said, 'but I'm in a hurry and this is quicker.'

'Don't apologise. I'm terribly grateful you brought me as far as here.'

He muttered a reply and shot away even as she was shutting the door.

152

'Who was that?' a Cockney voice asked.

Amanda swung round to see one of the other secretaries coming towards her.

'No one important,' she replied, and ran into the office.

CHAPTER TEN

As he anticipated, Mr. Craig was well enough to work with Amanda on Friday, and she spent the best part of the morning at his home. It did not need him to tell her that what he was dictating was highly confidential, for as her pencil flew over the pages of her notebook she knew that each hieroglyphic would be of infinite value to Clive. Here were all the facts and figures he was so anxious to know: the sites of the three hypermarkets which Homefare were negotiating to buy around London, and the location of three more they were planning in the Midlands.

'I'll give you the key to my desk,' Mr. Craig said when he had finished, 'and I'd like you to put the carbon copies in there. You'll find a blue file in the lower drawer into which they should go.'

'What about the report itself?' she asked. 'I take it you don't want it sent through the post?'

'Certainly not. When it's ready, get one of our senior messengers to take it to Mr. Foster.'

'I can do it myself.'

'That won't be necessary,' Mr. Craig said hurriedly.

Gathering her things together, Amanda stood up. 'I'll have it typed by mid-afternoon so Mr. Foster should receive it today.'

'Excellent.' Mr. Craig fumbled on his bedside table for his key-ring and prised off a small key as carefully as though he was handling a gold nugget. 'Mind you lock the desk again after you've put the carbons in it,' he warned.

Promising to obey his instructions, Amanda returned to the office. Going back in the subway she had resolutely kept her mind a blank, and even now, as she typed out the complicated figures and checked to see there were no errors, she was able to think only of what she was doing and not let any other thoughts come into her mind. Yet she knew this was only the calm before the storm, and that she would soon be faced with a decision which she had been dreading ever since Clive had first asked her to help him. Here at her disposal was information of vital importance to him: all that prevented her from giving it to him was her loyalty to Homefare.

'Why should I feel loyalty to a company that treated my father so badly?' The question loomed large in her mind; the same question that had been there for months. But this time the answer was different; perhaps because she was beginning to accept—indeed had already accepted—the fact that Homefare had not been unscrupulous in its dealings with the small grocery shops they had made redundant. She could no longer go on blaming them for her father's lack of business sense in deciding to fight them.

And if she did not blame them, then she owed them her undivided loyalty.

Calmly she took the top sheets, folded them and placed them into an envelope addressed to Charles Foster. Then she collected the carbons and walked into Mr. Craig's office. As she bent over the drawer to

154

unlock it, the telephone rang. She picked it up, almost dropping it in surprise as she heard her mother's voice. It took a moment for her to realise that the call came from Tangier.

'I had a letter from Clive,' Mrs. Stewart said. 'He wrote that you'd both be coming here for Christmas. It will be wonderful to see you again, darling.'

'I'm not absolutely positive I'm coming,' Amanda said cautiously.

'What's stopping you? Is it Red?'

Amanda sought for the right answer, but no words would come.

'Is there someone in the office with you, dear?' her mother asked. 'Is that why you can't talk?'

'Yes,' Amanda replied, grasping at the excuse proffered. 'It is rather difficult.'

'Then *I'll* talk to you.' Happily Mrs. Stewart did so, giving an account of her days at the nursing home —which sounded more like a luxury hotel—and of the people she had met and how well she felt. 'It's hard to believe I've been here so long,' she continued, 'and even harder still to think it's nearly Christmas. It's like a summer's day here.'

'That's just what you need,' said Amanda.

'You're so right: I've never felt better in my life, and it's all due to you.'

'Not me.'

'Well, you know what I mean. If Clive didn't love you. ... You will come out here for Christmas, won't you, dear?'

'Probably, but I'll write to you. I honestly can't talk now.'

She was shaking as she put down the receiver, and for a long time she remained looking at it, trying to marshal her thoughts. One thing was clear: her debt to Clive was a big one, and if there was any small way in which she could repay him, she had to do so. That was where her first duty lay: with Clive.

Not giving herself time to think, she picked up the carbon copy and put it into her handbag. Then she fled from the room as though all the bats in hell were after her.

If her bag had been holding a time-bomb, Amanda could not have been more conscious of it. Indeed, in her guilty state of mind the action she had just taken could well cause events to blow up in her face. If Clive acted on the information she gave him, would Mr. Craig realise what she had done, and if he did, would he be able to prosecute her? She tried to remember if she had ever heard of such a case, but nothing came to mind. Yet industrial espionage was a well-known activity: a career for scoundrels, it had once been called in a newspaper article. Never had she believed that one day she would be joining those unholy ranks.

As if her guilt was stamped on her face she refused to look at her reflection when she powdered her nose before leaving the office, and found it impossible to smile goodnight to the commissionaire at the front door lest he had X-ray eyes that could see into her mind and tell him what she was planning to do.

All the way home her handbag lay heavy in her lap, but no heavier than her heart, and entering the sitting-room she went straight to the sideboard and poured herself a sherry, drinking it down at a gulp. Now she knew why people took a drink to steady their nerves! Holding a second drink in her hand, she hurried into the bedroom to change. Clive was calling for her and she did not want to keep him waiting.

She was trembling with renewed force as, twenty minutes later, she peered through the window and saw his car draw to a stop outside the house. Not giving herself time to think, she ran downstairs, reaching the hall almost before he had rung the bell.

'I've been waiting for you,' she said breathlessly.

'So it seems.' He helped her into the car, talking in his usual quiet way.

She forced herself to concentrate on what he was saying, acutely aware of his blunt chin and dark, steady eyes that saw so much. Her hand went to her bag, curling tightly around the handle.

'What was your day like?' Clive asked.

She jumped as though he had shot her, and he looked at her in surprise.

'Anything wrong, Amanda? You're unusually pale.'

'I suppose I'm tired. I've been busy.'

'I thought your boss was away ill.'

'He is. But I—I did some work with him this morning. I went to his house.'

The second she spoke she knew she should have been quiet, for Clive was instantly on the alert.

'Why did you have to go *there*? Don't tell me Homefare can't run to a dictaphone!'

Here at last was the opportunity she had been waiting for. It was a simple matter to open her handbag, give Clive the papers and tell him to take a photostat before returning them to her. Her fingers moved on the clasp of her bag but her arm remained motionless. She could not do it; no matter what Clive had done for her mother, no matter how much money he had expended, she could not stoop to such dishonesty.

'Something *is* wrong,' said Clive, and drew the car into the kerb.

Amanda wondered dismally if she was fated to have all her dramatic scenes inside a car, and wished she had been able to reach her decision before Clive had picked her up. At least she could have then spoken to him in the flat—with the opportunity of moving out of his range should his anger become more than she could bear. But here she felt as pinned down as a butterfly on a board. An excellent simile, she thought dismally, as his eyes impaled her.

'What is it, Amanda? You're clutching your bag as if it's going to explode.'

She forced herself to let it drop to her lap, frighteningly aware that he could easily pull it away from her. Why, oh, why hadn't she left the carbons in the flat? But it was too late to think of that now. She slid back until she felt the handle of the door digging into her side.

'I can't do what you want,' she said breathlessly. 'You've been wonderful to my mother and I know I *ought* to do it, but I can't. I can't!'

'Can't do what?'

'Give you the information you want.'

'What information? Amanda, my dear, I don't know what you're talking about.'

'You do,' she said angrily, wondering if he were deliberately being obtuse. 'You want to know where Homefare are planning their next hypermarkets and I—I can't tell you. I mean I can,' she said distractedly, 'but I won't!'

Clive was so long in replying that her nerves grew tight with fear, but when he finally spoke his voice was unruffled.

'So that's why you've been like a cat on hot bricks since I picked you up. I take it from the way you've

158

been clutching your handbag that you actually have the information on you?' He swivelled round in his seat and she recoiled like a spring, the bag behind her back.

'I won't give it to you!' she cried.

'Then don't,' he said mildly. 'I told you the other day that I didn't expect you to do anything for me.'

'You *asked* me to spy,' she reminded him.

'When you first went to Homefare,' he agreed, 'but once I realised how strongly you felt about it, I told you to forget it.'

'You didn't mean it.'

'Perhaps not, but I said it and that meant I was giving you an out.'

'You knew I wouldn't take it.'

'You're taking it now.'

'Yes,' she sighed, 'I am. Oh, Clive, I'm sorry. You've been so good to my mother that——'

'Don't say you're grateful! The one thing you've never been is trite.'

It was his first sign of irritation and she was pleased by it. It was easier to stick to her resolution when he was angry rather than when he looked distressed.

'Let's drop the subject,' he said. 'Take the papers back and forget the whole thing. *I* have.'

'Don't be angry with me, Clive.'

'My dear, I'm not. I have all the information I need anyway. I had it several days ago.'

He switched on the engine and turned to face the road. She looked at his profile and wished she could read his thoughts, but his face was shuttered and gave nothing away.

His reaction surprised her and she began to analyse it. How had he learned about the costings when she herself had only had them from Mr. Craig that morning? The answer was horrifyingly clear. Red had told him. When she had seen him at Mr. Craig's house earlier in the week, he must have discussed it: that was why he had gone to Clive's house that same evening: to give him the all-important figures.

Before she could stop herself, she burst into tears. 'Take me home,' she cried, 'I don't want to go out.'

Sensing that she had reached the end of her tether, Clive did as she asked. All the way back to the flat she sat huddled in her seat, not speaking or moving, and only as he went to take her bag and get out her front door key did she jerk away from him and do it herself, her cheeks flaming as the look on his face told her he knew why she wouldn't let him have the handbag.

'You really do see me as an ogre,' he said, repeating a remark he had made not long ago. 'There must be something wrong with me, Amanda, that you should be so frightened of me.'

'There's nothing wrong with you, Clive. I'm the one at fault.'

Silently he followed her up the stairs and, once in the sitting-room, took off his coat and went over to the tray of drinks. If he noticed the glass on it, still half filled with sherry, he made no comment, but poured out two more and handed her one before lifting his own.

'Let's drink to our future, Amanda, and forget the past.'

'Your future, Clive, not ours.'

'What exactly does that mean?'

'I think you know.'

He paled visibly. 'Actually I've known it for some time, but I've been trying not to admit it. I kept telling myself you were shy of me; that you were worried because of the difference in our ages, or because I'd been married before.'

'Your age or your marriage has nothing to do with it,' she said hurriedly. 'It's just that I don't love you the way you deserve to be loved.'

'If you love me the way I deserved,' he said whimsically, 'you wouldn't love me at all—which of course you don't!'

She was too near to tears to smile at the quip, and realised he was using humour as his own safety valve. 'I wish it could have been different, Clive.'

'So do I.' He twirled the glass in his hand. 'There's no reason why we can't see each other. The fact that you don't love me shouldn't make any difference.'

'You know it would.'

'I don't want you to go out of my life.' His voice was loud and shaking. 'I love you, Amanda. I loved you the minute I saw you looking like some Indian goddess surrounded by all those ordinary girls.'

'I'm an ordinary girl myself. Don't be fooled by the feathers.'

'I'm not.' He took a step towards her, but her instinctive movement away from him made him stop. 'Don't I mean anything to you?' he asked.

'I nearly love you,' she said slowly, 'but not enough.'

'Is there anyone else?'

She was glad she had a glass to hold, for it prevented her shaking hands from being noticeable. If she owed Clive nothing else, she owed him this lie. 'There's no one else, Clive.'

'Then there's still hope for me.'

'No,' she said quickly. 'Please don't ask me to marry you again.'

'I won't need to do that. You know how I feel about you, and if you should change your mind. . . .' He saw her head shake and he sighed. 'I take it our trip to Tangier is off?'

'You wouldn't want to take me now, would you?'

'Why not? At least I'd be with you for Christmas.'

She caught her breath. 'You make me feel such a beast. Oh, Clive, I'm sorry.'

'Does that mean you'll let the arrangement stand?'

'I couldn't. It wouldn't be fair. I'd keep hating myself and . . . No, Clive.'

'Very well.' He braced his shoulders. 'You look all in, my darling, have an early night.'

Only as the door closed behind him did she realise he had not said goodbye. Was it because he had forgotten or because he did not want to do so? Either way, it would make no difference. She could never marry him. She should have told him so weeks ago. Her initial hesitancy alone should have made her realise she didn't love him enough. Yet though she felt a great sense of relief, she knew she would not be completely free of guilt towards him until she had repaid the money he had expended on her mother.

Anticipating a sleepless night, Amanda slept unusually heavily, and it was after ten when she awoke. The second her eyes rested on the handbag on the dressing table she was out of bed and opening it to look at the carbon copy, then glanced nervously at the window as though there was a man with a telescopic lens hidden in the trees opposite. No one could hide behind bare branches, she thought light-heartedly, and padded into the kitchen to make herself some breakfast. With a cup of tea in one hand and a slice of toast in the other, she went back to the bedroom and looked

162

at the folded white paper. She would not rest until she had restored it to Mr. Craig's desk.

What had she done with the key he had given her? Feverishly she rummaged in her handbag. It wasn't there! Panic made the blood run from her head and her scalp tingled. What had she done with it? If she had lost it ...

Her brow cleared and she laughed shakily. What a fool she was! She had changed her bag when she had changed her dress last night, and the key was still in the bag she used during the day. Sighing with relief, she picked it up. Saturday or no Saturday, she was going to go down to the office to put this all-important carbon copy into its rightful place.

CHAPTER ELEVEN

IT was easy for Amanda to contemplate putting the carbons back where they belonged when she was safely ensconced in her flat, but a far more nerve-racking proposition to actually do so, and as she approached the glass and steel structure that was Homefare, she nearly turned tail and fled. How imposing the building looked without any cars around it to mar its elegant steel lines. Though she had only worked for the company for a matter of months, it had become much more a part of her life than Brands had ever done. Here, the staff were encouraged to feel they had a say in the running of the organisation: a directive from Charles Foster no doubt. Though he himself did not mix with his employees, he insisted that all his senior personnel did, and everyone was kept informed of all new plans concerning the group. No secretary or messenger boy had to read a newspaper to find out what was going on inside their company. Had the progress of this mammoth organisation not disrupted her own life so disastrously, she could well have enjoyed working for them.

She sighed as she thought of Red—he was synonymous with Homefare. One day she might tell him the real reason she had refused to marry him. How would he feel when he discovered that for the sake of a few hundred or a few thousand pounds he had lost her? Perhaps by then he would no longer care. She remembered the pretty blonde she had seen with him in the restaurant, and bitterness soured her thoughts.

She reached the main doors and, seeing they were closed, pushed at one of the smaller side ones. These were closed too, and she looked round for a bell. There were none to be seen and she wondered how to attract the attention of the security guard who patrolled the building. It had never occurred to her that she would not be able to get up to her office. She frowned, not sure whether to go home and come back again early on Monday or hang around on the off-chance that the guard would eventually walk through the foyer and see her. Deciding to wait for a while, she remained by the door.

Time passed and the cold began to seep into her bones. It was a dull day, the dark skies indicating snow to come, and she blew into her gloves to keep her hands warm and stamped her feet on the ground to stop them getting numb. She was about to give up and go home when she saw a reflection in the glass. Peering through it, she made out a uniformed figure. Knowing her voice would not be heard through the thick panes, she banged on the door. The man seemed oblivious of her presence and she banged harder, making her knuckles tingle. To her relief he noticed her and came forward and stared through the glass. Luckily he was a guard she had seen from time to time during the week—had he not recognised her she knew she would have stood no chance of getting in—but with a smile he unlocked the door for her to do so.

'I didn't know who you were for a minute,' he remarked. 'Come to collect something?'

'Yes.'

Unwilling to stand there talking to him, Amanda moved towards the staircase and, ignoring the lift, raced up to the second floor. Though she had frequently left the office after everyone else, she had never been in the building when it was totally deserted and she could not help noticing how eerie it looked.

She pushed open the door of her office and ran straight through to Mr. Craig's. Bending over his desk, she inserted the key in the lock and turned it. The lock refused to budge and carefully she turned the key again, exerting firm pressure until there was a rasping sound and the lock was completely released. With fast beating heart she slid open the drawer.

Inside were several files and a stack of papers, but it was the blue file she wanted and she took it out and opened it. Putting her hand in her bag, she touched the carbon copy of the report she had typed for Mr. Craig yesterday. A faint sound made her straighten sharply and she looked towards the reeded glass door leading to the outer office. It was several inches ajar and even as she watched it, it opened several inches more. Her scalp tingled and she waited tensely, not sure what to expect and chiding herself for being

165

afraid. It could only be the security officer whose curiosity had got the better of him.

The door opened to its full width and the man who stepped into the room brought the blood to her cheeks. What was Red doing here, and how long had he been watching her? Her mind raced ahead as she tried to find suitable answers to any questions he might ask, but when he did speak, his voice was so soft that she had to strain to hear it.

'What are you doing here, Amanda?'

'That's my line,' she said with commendable coolness. 'What are *you* doing here?'

'I asked first.' He moved forward **and** she was intensely aware of her hand still in her handbag. Her fingers curled around the copy of the report: the copy which should be inside the blue folder. Not that Red knew this, she reminded herself. The thought was calming and gave her the courage to stare at him haughtily.

'What are you doing in Mr. Craig's office?' she demanded. 'You know very well there's no one here on a Saturday.'

'I came to see what *you* were doing here. I was leaving the building when Rogers told me he'd let you in.'

'And you came to wish me good morning, no doubt?'

'I came to see what you were doing,' he repeated, and this time stared pointedly at her hand which was still hidden in her bag. 'Were you taking something out or putting something in?' he asked equably.

'That's none of your business.'

'On the contrary.' With a speed that caught her unawares, he reached out and snapped her bag shut, imprisoning her hand. The clasp dug into her flesh and she gave a cry of pain.

'You're hurting me!'

'Sorry.' Without looking in the least apologetic he unloosened the bag for her to take out her hand. But his fingers remained on hers, tight as a vice, preventing her from releasing the sheet of paper she was clutching.

'What were you doing with that paper?' he asked. 'Taking it out of Mr. Craig's desk or putting it back?'

'I was putting it back.'

'Is that why you came rushing down here this morning like a scalded cat?'

'I forgot to put it away last night,' she said in a tight voice, 'and as it was highly confidential I came down this morning to do it. I felt uneasy keeping it at home.'

'How conscientious of you, Amanda.' Red unfolded the paper as he spoke. He glanced at it and his skin was slowly blanched of colour. 'I can see why you didn't want to leave it in your flat. It could be very important to the right person.'

'*You* should know,' she said bitterly.

'I do.'

She went to take the paper from him, but he stepped back with it and shook his head. 'Not so fast, Amanda. I want to know if you showed this to anyone.'

'I don't know what you're talking about.' Her reply was immediate, but she could not prevent the scarlet colour from rushing into her face. It gave her away, broadcasting what she was desperately trying to hide.

'I think you do know,' he said, and all at once looked infinitely weary. His eyes lost their blue glitter and became opaque, as though shutters had come down over them. 'You didn't forget to put this paper away yesterday; you deliberately took it home with you in order to give it to Clive Brand.'

'You're mad!'

'Is that why you came to work here?' Red went on as if he had not heard her interruption. 'So that you could spy for him? Is that his only interest in you, or does he really want to marry you?'

'He loves me,' Amanda cried, 'and I'm not spying for him!'

'Then why did you take this report home, and why are you trying to sneak it back like a thief? For heaven's sake don't lie to me, Amanda, I can see the truth in your face.'

'What truth?' she burst out. 'You don't even know the meaning of the word. How dare you accuse me of being a spy when you're no better yourself?'

'What do you mean by that?' He gripped her arm, but she shook him free.

'You know very well what I mean. I've *seen* you with Clive! I saw you twice in his car and one evening I saw you leaving his house. So don't accuse me of spying when you're doing exactly the same!'

'So that's it!' He caught hold of her again and shook her so violently that her hair fell around her shoulders. 'So *I'm* the one who's giving away Homefare secrets, am I?'

'Yes!' she stormed, beside herself with rage and hurt. 'That's why Clive didn't need my help any more —because you'd already told him what he wanted to know.'

'So you *were* going to tell him.' Red's face was within an inch of hers, and she saw a film of perspiration on his upper lip.

'I wasn't going to tell him,' she whispered. 'I couldn't do it.'

'You mean it wasn't necessary.'

'No—not that. I meant I couldn't go through with it.'

'Do you expect me to believe you?'

'It's the truth. I swear it.'

'You should cry when you say that!' Red taunted. 'It might make me believe you.' He flung her away from him so violently that she hit the side of the desk. 'You're a cheat and a liar, Amanda. I should have guessed why you came to work here the minute I found out you knew Clive Brand.'

'He wants to marry me,' she said. 'That's why I'm seeing him.'

'What's stopping you from marrying him—is he saving up for a special licence?'

'Oh!' she gave an angry exclamation. 'You know why I haven't said yes!'

'You're damn right I do! You came here to spy for him and you wouldn't leave until you'd finished your dirty work.'

'That's not true! Clive never knew I was taking a job here. I came to Homefare without telling him. When he fell in love with me he didn't want me to work at Brands. I thought he was being silly about it and I deliberately took a job with his rivals.'

'With no ulterior motive, I suppose?' Red was still scornful. 'You're a poor liar, Amanda, but then you're not much good at anything. You even let yourself get caught *returning* information! It's a pity I had to come here this morning and spoil your little game. You won't be able to stay here now, will you?'

'I wasn't going to stay.'

'Bad conscience, Amanda, or doesn't Clive need you here any more?'

'Clive had nothing to do with my decision.' She saw

the disbelief on Red's face and her voice went high with anger. 'How dare you look at me like that? I've a good mind to tell Mr. Craig about you and Clive.'

'What's stopping you? If you were so concerned about Homefare you would have done so long before now.' Red was the one who was shouting now, his whole attention focused on her, unaware that the security guard had come in to see what the commotion was about.

'Be quiet, Red!' Amanda cried, and moved in front of the open drawer to hide it.

The guard took a step backwards, looking distinctly uncomfortable. 'I didn't realise you were here, sir,' he said to Red. 'I heard the shouting and I came to see if there was any trouble.'

'There's no trouble,' Red answered.

'Very good, sir. If you could give me some idea when you'll be leaving, I'll wait in the downstairs hall. It's my tea break, but I won't take it till I've seen you off the premises.'

'I'll only be a few minutes,' Red said curtly.

'There's no hurry, Mr. Foster,' the guard said quickly. 'No hurry at all.' He gave a half-salute and backed out, closing the door behind him.

Dumbfounded, Amanda gazed at Red. She knew she had heard correctly, yet she could not believe it. Yet if there had been any doubt in her mind, one look at Red's face would have told her the truth.

'Are you—*you're* Charles Foster?' she whispered.

'Yes.'

'You mean you—you own ... All the time you were taking me out you were lying—pretending that ... You're not an estate agent?'

170

'That part happens to be true. I *am* a qualified surveyor.'

'But you run Homefare.'

'I find sites for the company too.'

'You know what I mean,' she said shakily. 'You've been fooling me.'

'No more than you were fooling my company,' he retorted.

'Is that why you went on seeing me?' she whispered. 'Because you suspected me?' He did not answer and her bitterness intensified. 'I see it all now. At first your pretence was a game—a joke you were playing on some silly little girl who didn't know you were the almighty Charles Foster. But when you found out I knew Clive you thought he'd put me here to spy.'

'I suspected it.'

Words failed her and she struggled to continue. Rage and hurt fought inside her, but neither won and, rendered speechless by the battle, she picked up her bag and ran out of the room, intent only on escape, on never seeing Red again.

If Amanda's thoughts had been in a turmoil after Clive had left her last night, it was nothing compared with the anguish she felt now, and it was several hours before she was in a fit state to think logically.

Red was Charles Foster. Incredible though it was, casually dressed, laconic Red Clark was the mastermind behind Homefare. What a laugh he must have had every time he had taken her out! It showed much for his acting ability that he hadn't given himself away, nor would he have done today if the security guard had not done it for him.

As the afternoon gave way to evening, Amanda tried to make more sense out of all she had learned, but

171

too many questions remained unanswered. Why had Red asked her to marry him without admitting his identity? Was it because he hadn't meant it, or had he been afraid that if she knew who he was she might have been blinded by his money? Remembering the reason she had given for turning him down, she burned with shame. How stupidly she had played into his hands, making it easy for him to believe she was only interested in wealth.

Yet she had not wanted to tell Red the real reason she could not marry him. Memory flooded through her; painful, heart-breaking memories that only yesterday had threatened to tear her apart and were now seen to be totally invalid.

Her reason for not marrying Red no longer existed. The knowledge astonished her, bringing a new dimension into her life. If Red was Charles Foster this made nonsense of her belief that he had been selling Home-fare secrets to Clive! But if this was not so, why had the two men met surreptitiously and then lied about it? She could understand Red doing so—it would have destroyed his pretence of working for Brands—but the same reason did not apply to Clive. She remembered the lead she had given him the other night when she had seen Red leave his house. Why hadn't he told her then that he had seen Charles Foster?

She perched on the edge of a chair, trying to recollect exactly what she had said to him and his exact words in reply. Slowly the conversation returned, and with it came enlightenment. When she had told Clive she knew the man who had left his house, he had assumed she had known it was his biggest business competitor; he had not realised she only knew him as Red Clark. But this still did not explain the reasons for their meetings, nor Clive's insistence that she told no one about them. Obviously the two men had met in their capacity as the heads of two rival groups, though why, was something she could not even begin to guess.

Hard on this thought came the knowledge of how badly she had misjudged Clive. Even yesterday when he had told her not to give him any information if she considered it disloyal to Homefare, she had cynically believed he had said it because he already had the information from Red. Now she knew this to be untrue. Clive had genuinely meant what he said.

Her anger against Red mounted. His charade had not only hurt her, but Clive too, and she felt she owed him an apology. If only she could return his love! But bright blue eyes blazing with scorn could not be eradicated from her mind, and even the knowledge that Red had made a fool of her did not destroy her need of him. She despised him, almost hated him, but she could not stop loving him.

CHAPTER TWELVE

The look on Clive's face when she walked into his drawing-room an hour later was so full of hope that Amanda almost regretted her visit.

'I haven't changed my mind,' she said at once. 'I came because there's something I want to tell you.'

Momentarily he looked at a loss. Then he came forward and escorted her to a chair. 'I always seem to be asking you what's wrong,' he said quietly.

'Nothing's wrong. I came here to apologise.'

'For refusing to marry me?'

'It's about one of my reasons for refusing.' She saw he was not following her and she hurried on: 'I didn't realise you knew Charles Foster. I thought you knew him as Red. That's why I was so upset.'

'Red?' Clive was still perplexed.

'Yes. Red Clark. That's the name I knew him by. I met him in Mr. Craig's office and he told me that was his name. I didn't discover his real identity until this morning.'

Clive was looking incredulous. 'Who was he pretending to be?'

'An estate agent. He said his job was to find sites for Homefare. It's not funny,' she said sharply as she saw Clive's mouth twitch.

'Sorry, my dear, but knowing Charles Foster, it's just the sort of thing he *would* say. His sense of humour isn't mine.'

'Nor mine,' she said angrily. 'When I think of the way he fooled me; the way he took me out and pretended ...' Her voice died away as she saw Clive's expression.

'It seems you've been seeing quite a bit of him,' he said dryly.

'Not all that much.' She forced herself to continue. 'I thought it would help me to—to make up my mind about you if I went out with someone else.'

'You don't need to apologise for going out with another man. I never asked you not to do so.'

'*You* never went out with anyone else.'

'Because I had no doubts about my feelings for you.' He took a cigar from a box on the table and carefully clipped off one end with a gold cigar cutter. 'How did you find out he was Charles Foster? Did he tell you?'

Amanda had been dreading this question, but she

braced herself to answer it. Carefully she recounted the whole story, beginning with her decision to return the carbon copy to Mr. Craig's desk that morning and concluding with the entry of the security guard, whose recognition of Red had given away his identity.

'It's quite a saga,' Clive commented as she finished.

Amanda nodded, wondering what he would say if he knew all of it. But to tell him that Red had asked her to marry him—and why she had refused—would serve no purpose other than to hurt him.

'It was an odd sort of game for him to have played,' Clive went on, leaning one elbow on the mantelpiece and warming himself by the fire. 'But then, as I said before, he has a strange sense of humour. He takes the most unexpected things seriously, and many serious things unexpectedly.'

'I know what you mean,' she said bitterly.

'Still, the only harm done is that you can't stay at Homefare.' He put out a hand. 'I wish you'd let me help you financially. There'd be no strings attached to it.'

'No, Clive, I've already taken more than enough from you. If there was any way I could repay you for what you've done for my mother——'

'No, Amanda.' He was by her side, bending down to stare into her face. 'Being able to help your mother is the only way I can show you how much I love you. Don't throw it back at me; and for heaven's sake stop worrying about it.'

'But I——'

'Would you have a sleepless night if you gave me five pounds?'

'Of course not.'

'Then think of it in those terms. What I've expended on your mother has the relative value to me.'

With all her heart Amanda wished she could tell Clive she loved him. How happy he would be if she agreed to marry him. The temptation to at least make one person happy was so strong that she almost said, 'Yes, I *will* be your wife.' But then Clive turned back to the fireplace and, in moving away, broke the spell that her chaotic thoughts had cast upon her, making her realise that to marry him out of gratitude would eventually bring unhappiness to both of them. Knowing there was nothing more she could say, she moved to the door.

'What are you going to do?' he asked.

'I'm not sure.'

'Will you let me send you to Tangier for Christmas? It would be a shame to disappoint your mother.'

Though pride wanted her to refuse, she would not allow herself the luxury. 'Thank you, Clive,' she whispered, 'that would be wonderful.'

She was at the door when he spoke to her again.

'If you should change your mind about me, Amanda, don't be too embarrassed to come and tell me.'

'I would never be embarrassed to tell you I loved you. But I won't change my mind, Clive, it wouldn't be fair to you.'

Her second parting from him left her infinitely sadder than her first one, and the sadness remained upon her like a shroud.

On Monday morning at eight o'clock a Homefare messenger delivered a letter to her, and seeing the boy on the doorstep she knew exactly why he had come. Opening the letter confirmed her belief. It was an official dismissal and requested her not to return to the office. There was also a cheque for three months' salary, and without giving herself time to think, she put it in an envelope, addressed it to Charles Foster at his office in Mayfair and went out to post it. How dare he insult her one minute and send her three months' salary the next?

The act of writing his name brought him vividly to mind, and it became a losing battle not to think of him. She could see why a man with his particular humour would have been amused by the rude way she had treated him on the first occasion they had met—especially when she had half suspected him of being a thief—and knew that had she been in his shoes she would probably have done the same. But she would never have had the strength of mind to continue the subterfuge for so long, nor to have done so once her liking had turned to love. The thought made her wonder how deep his love for her had been. It was certainly not based on understanding or trust, for he had felt neither one nor shown the other, and it was this knowledge which hurt her more than anything else. Still, she could not spend the rest of her life thinking of Charles Foster, alias Red Clark. She had to find another job in a company where she would not be reminded of the past unhappy months.

With Christmas only a week away it was pointless to look for a job, and she spent the few days before she was due to leave for Tangier in cleaning the flat and buying Christmas presents, using some of her careful savings to do so.

The days dragged slowly by, but the nights were even worse, for piercing blue eyes and red hair haunted her dreams. But at last it was the day of her flight, and hoping that when she left England she would also leave behind the memories that were tormenting her, Amanda boarded the plane.

Clive had booked her first class, and though she appreciated the extra comfort and enjoyed the champagne and caviar, she could not help thinking what a waste of money it was, and how much she herself had given up by refusing to become Mrs. Clive Brand. What would her mother say when she heard about it? Thinking of the explanations she would have to give—and she would certainly have to tell her mother of Red's true identity—she almost wished she had not come to Tangier. But explanations would have to be made sooner or later, and perhaps the sooner they were done, the more quickly she would be able to forget Red.

The flight was uneventful, as was the journey from the airport to Tangier itself, though it was early evening before she reached the nursing home.

It was not at all the way she had imagined it, being a large, Moorish-style house set in beautiful grounds on a hill overlooking the town. Inside it was like a luxury hotel, and though several of the patients were in dressing-gowns, most of them wore casual clothes. Mrs. Stewart looked younger and more rested than Amanda ever remembered seeing her, and this, more than anything else, put an end to any regrets she had at accepting Clive's help. What did pride matter when her mother looked so well?

'I'm sorry Clive wasn't able to come with you,' Mrs. Stewart said a little later, as they sat sipping strong, sweet coffee on the balcony of her room. 'He wrote me a very sweet letter, you know, and said you would be telling me why he wasn't here.' She hesitated. 'I suppose you decided you didn't want to marry him?'

'Yes.'

'Are you sure you were wise to turn him down?'

'It would have been wrong to do anything else.'

'Because you're in love with Red?'

This was the opening Amanda had been waiting for, though she wished it had come a little later, when she had had a chance to compose herself. 'There's something you should know about Red,' she began, and rushed into the story without giving herself any more time to think.

'My poor child,' Mrs. Stewart muttered as she came to the end. 'It's the sort of muddled-up tragedy that Shakespeare would have turned into a comedy!'

'It hasn't been very comic for me,' Amanda retorted. 'The only good thing about it is that it's over and done with. I never want to talk about it again.'

'Do you really think Red won't try to see you?'

'It would make no difference if he did. If you'd seen his face when he found me in the office ...' Amanda clenched her hands in an effort to control her angry tears. 'Nothing I said could convince him I'd changed my mind about showing that carbon copy to Clive.'

'But you were putting the report *back*.'

'He said I was doing it because Clive didn't need it.'

'Of course he needed it,' Mrs. Stewart insisted. 'How else could he get the costings?'

'But Clive *didn't* want the report; he told me so himself.' Amanda frowned. 'That's odd. I thought Red had sold him the information, but if Red is Charles Foster ...' The frown grew deeper. 'Then how *did* Clive find out what the costings were?'

'Perhaps he had someone else spying for him.'

'I doubt it.'

'Well, it doesn't matter now. It's over and done with.'

'You're right, darling.' Amanda forced a smile to

179

her lips. 'Don't let's talk about either of them any more.'

But words were said more easily than deeds were done, and for the next few days Amanda thought frequently about both the men. Clive had spared no expense in ensuring she enjoyed her holiday here. Not only had he booked her a suite in the best hotel, but he had arranged for a car and chauffeur to be at her disposal, and had given strict instructions that she was not to be allowed to explore the city on her own. More than ever she realised what being married to him would have meant. What cosseting she would have received, what care and devotion. Yet it was this very aspect of Clive's behaviour which had worried her so much, for she had always felt he regarded her as a beautiful possession to be cherished rather than as a person with whom to share his thoughts and innermost life. Marriage to Red would have brought no such cosseting; and no happiness either, she reminded herself. He had teased her and provoked her and had driven her wild with his casualness. He had also lied to her and called her a spy.

Resolutely she fought against the tears, and concentrated on the goods displayed on the stall in front of her. She had decided to spend the morning looking for bargains, and all she had done so far was to waste time thinking of the two men she wanted to forget.

A small, gilded mirror winked up at her—exactly the gee-gaw her mother would like—and on an impulse she bought it and took it with her to the nursing home that afternoon.

'What do you think of the news?' her mother greeted her as she came on to the shaded veranda which overlooked the garden, where flowers bloomed in a riot of gaudy colour.

'What news? I haven't seen any newspapers since I got here.'

'It's in *The Times*,' her mother explained. 'Look on the table behind you.'

Amanda picked up the airmail edition. As usual, the headlines were political, and she glanced through them quickly.

'On the next page,' Mrs. Stewart said, and Amanda opened the paper.

A picture of Clive and Red stared up at her. 'Take-Over Surprises City' she read, and with fast-beating heart scanned the rest of the article. So this was why Clive and Red had been meeting in secret; why Clive had warned her not to tell anyone she had seen them together, and why Red himself had made no reference to knowing Clive even when she had given him a chance to do so.

In a take-over bid involving millions of pounds, Homefare was buying Brands. 'We do not anticipate making any major changes,' Mr. Charles Foster assured all the employees of the newly acquired company, she read, 'and any redundancies due to reorganisation will be amply compensated.' Only at the end of the article did Amanda learn that Clive was returning to Canada. 'I have been extremely happy during my stay in England,' he stated, 'but personal reasons have decided me to make my home in Canada again.'

It was chastening for Amanda to realise that she was the personal reason to whom Clive was referring. Reading the full-page report about him suddenly highlighted his importance and wealth, as it did for Red. Red. She stared at his photograph. Even in black and white it made him look incredibly handsome; and different too, for he wore a faultlessly tailored suit. It had taken the importance of a press conference to get him to put on a collar and tie! Quickly she closed the paper and set it down.

'You could still go to Canada,' Mrs. Stewart said.

'How about my going with you for a walk instead?' Amanda suggested, and taking the hint, her mother went with her into the garden.

As she had expected, Amanda spent a restless night. Seeing Red's photograph re-awakened all her love for him, and though she chided herself for being a fool, she could not help thinking of all she had lost. How happy she and Red could have been if he had trusted her; or if she had trusted him! A knife seemed to turn in her breast. She was furious with him for doubting her integrity, yet she had done exactly the same with him. Had she not believed him to be a spy, she would have accepted his proposal. With a cry she buried her head in the pillow.

The morning sunshine dispelled her gloom, and forcing herself to believe that time would end her love for Red, she put on one of her prettiest dresses—lemon cotton with a wide neckline that showed her delicate tan—and went downstairs. She rarely went to see her mother until mid-morning, and decided to read a book in the shade of one of the palms in the garden.

Reclining in a cane chair—the warmth of the sun dispelled by the canopy of leaves overhead—she turned the pages of her book without being aware of what she was reading. The strident cries of cicadas broke the stillness around her, and the deep blue sky above was occasionally disturbed by the vapour trail of a jet. The air shimmered with heat and even the heads of the flowers drooped, making Amanda feel tired too, so that the book slipped from her fingers and she closed her eyes.

It was not a sound, so much as an awareness of being watched, that made her open them again. Long legs attired in silk mohair slacks were crossed negligently one over the other, and her eyes travelled the length of them until they reached the fine cream silk shirt, then higher still to see a tanned column of throat, curling mouth and quizzical, deep blue eyes.

With a sharp catch of breath she went to rise, intent only on escape, but Red's arm came across the front of her chair, making it impossible for her to move.

'Oh no, you don't,' he said softly. 'I've come too far to have you run out on me now. You and I are going to have a little talk.'

'I have nothing to say to you.'

'I'm delighted to hear it. It will at least give me a chance to talk to *you*; and I've plenty to say.'

'I don't want to hear it.' She turned her eyes away from him and stared at the grass.

'Before I start,' he said, 'I want to tell you how sorry I am for what I said to you the last time we met. If kneeling at your feet will make you believe me, I'll willingly go down on my knees.'

'You could crawl on your stomach and I wouldn't believe you!' she retorted, and tried to stand. The movement brought her up against his arm and she felt it hard and sinewy on her breasts. Hurriedly she crouched back in the chair. 'All right,' she whispered, 'I'll accept your apology. Now please go.'

'I don't only want you to accept my apology, Amanda. I want you to forgive me.'

'Forgive you for thinking I was going to steal your

secrets?' Her head tilted proudly. 'I *was* stealing the report. You saw it in my bag; what more proof do you want?'

'You were putting it back.'

'Because Clive didn't need to know what was in it,' she reminded him. 'When I read *The Times* yesterday I realised why he didn't need my help.'

A flicker of embarrassment crossed Red's face, but he did not let it deter him from answering her remark. 'Even if Clive *had* wanted to know about the report you wouldn't have told him. When it came to the crunch you'd never have given away confidential information.'

'What makes you so sure?' she asked scornfully. 'You thought exactly the opposite the last time you saw me.'

'Because I was furious with you and I wasn't thinking straight.'

'And now you are?'

'Yes.'

'Ten days later? It's taken you a long time to come to your senses.'

'I've been trying to get hold of you for a week,' he burst out. 'Mrs. Chadwalla refused to tell me where you were, and when I telephoned your mother she flatly denied you were here.'

'My mother denied it?'

'She damned well did! She can lie as well as you can!'

Astonished that her mother had done so, and also kept Red's telephone call a secret, Amanda remained silent.

'Don't sit there staring at me with those big blue eyes,' he said, 'or I won't have the strength to finish what I want to say.' He drew his arm away from her chair and stood up. 'After we had that scene in the office it took a couple of days for my temper to cool. When it did, I knew what a fool I'd been. That's when I tried to see you. I knew that no matter what Clive had offered you, you wouldn't spy for him. You weren't that sort of person.'

Amanda had never thought she would hear Red speak like this, nor had she thought to see him looking at her with such longing. There was no humour on his face; none of the quizzical teasing she had considered so much a part of his character. He was serious and intent, as though determined to make her believe he meant what he said; yet she could not give in to him so quickly. It was not as easy as he wanted her to believe.

'Why didn't you tell me who you were,' she demanded, 'when you asked me to marry you?'

Embarrassment creased his face and he ran his hand through his hair. 'My only excuse is that I was a romantic fool. I fell for you the minute I saw you and I wanted to be sure your feeling for me was just as real. I've had several affairs,' he confessed, 'and it's made me cynical where women are concerned. That's why I didn't want you to know my identity.' A glint stirred in his eyes. 'You gave me a pretty bad time with your rich boy-friend. When it turned out to be Clive Brand I felt like murdering you.'

'You were quick to assume I was going to marry him,' she retorted.

'You wanted me to believe it.' He bent over her again, blocking her way. 'Why did you do that?'

'Because I saw you with Clive and I thought you were selling out the company you were working for.'

His eyes widened. 'So that was it! If only you'd told me you'd seen me.'

'I kept hinting.'

'I guess I'm too thick-skinned to take a hint,' he said ruefully. 'We'd have saved ourselves a lot of heartache if I had.'

She did not know what to say, and so said the first thing that came into her head. 'How did you find me?'

'Through Clive. I met him yesterday to sign the final documents, and by then I was so desperate to know where you were that I asked him.'

Though Red spoke casually, Amanda guessed what it must have cost him in pride to ask Clive's help, and at the same time was able to spare a thought to Clive's generosity in giving it.

'Poor Clive,' she whispered.

'Don't feel sorry for *him*,' Red said roughly. 'Feel sorry for me.' In a violent gesture he pulled her up from the chair and took her into his arms. 'I love you, Amanda. I have no life without you. Don't send me away.'

'I couldn't even if I wanted to.' Her voice was so low he had to lean close to hear it. 'I've been so miserable without you. Life hasn't seemed worth living.'

'I know how you feel,' he said huskily, and rubbed his cheek against hers. 'But if I hadn't come after you, you wouldn't have come to *me*.'

'No, I wouldn't,' she replied. 'You can't have love without faith, and if you hadn't found faith in me, we would never have been happy together.'

He looked into her eyes and saw his reflection there. 'I'll never doubt you again, my darling.'

'Do you promise to cherish me and cosset me and never tease me again either?'

'I'll do anything you want of me,' he murmured against her mouth. 'You're my own little radish-head!'

Her laughing protest died beneath the touch of his lips, for the humour of his words was belied by the urgent longing of his embrace, the trembling of his body and the heavy thudding of his heart. Her mouth parted beneath his and she returned his kisses with unrestrained passion, knowing she had no need to be afraid of him, for in this man's arms she was at home and wanted to be nowhere else.

'We have so much lost time to make up,' his lips moved on hers, as though he were reluctant to raise them even for a moment. 'We'll fly back to England tomorrow and get married by special licence the day after.'

'So soon?' she asked, and seeing the look in his eyes began to tremble.

'I'd make it sooner if it were possible,' he said hoarsely. 'I'd like our first-born to be legitimate, my darling, beautiful Amanda, and he won't be if we don't get married at once.'

Laughter lessened her shyness. 'That's the first time you've ever called me beautiful.' She wound her arms around his neck and pressed tightly against him. 'I'll fly back home with you tonight, if you like.'

'Because I called you beautiful?'

'Because of Red or Amanda junior,' she whispered, and heard in his triumphant laugh an echo of the happy years ahead.

What the press says about Harlequin romance fiction...

"When it comes to romantic novels...
Harlequin is the indisputable king."
—*New York Times*

"'Harlequin [is]... the best and the biggest.'"
—*Associated Press* (quoting Janet Dailey's husband, Bill)

"The most popular reading matter of
American women today."
—*Detroit News*

"... exciting escapism, easy reading, interesting
characters and, always, a happy ending....
They are hard to put down."
—*Transcript-Telegram*, Holyoke (Mass.)

"... a work of art."
—*Globe & Mail*, Toronto

Take these best-selling novels

4

FREE

Harlequin Presents

ANNE HAMPSON
gates of steel

ANNE MATHER
sweet revenge

VIOLET WINSPEAR
devil in a silver room

JANET DAILEY
no quarter asked

Harlequin Presents...

Take these
4 best-selling novels
FREE

as advertised on TV

That's right! FOUR first-rate Harlequin romance novels by four world renowned authors, FREE, as your introduction to the Harlequin Presents Subscription Plan. Be swept along by these FOUR exciting, poignant and sophisticated novels . . . . Travel to the Mediterranean island of Cyprus in **Anne Hampson**'s "Gates of Steel" . . . to Portugal for **Anne Mather**'s "Sweet Revenge" . . . to France and **Violet Winspear**'s "Devil in a Silver Room" . . . and the sprawling state of Texas for **Janet Dailey**'s "No Quarter Asked."

Join the millions of avid Harlequin readers all over the world who delight in the magic of a really exciting novel. EIGHT great NEW titles published EACH MONTH! Each month you will get to know exciting, interesting, true-to-life people . . . . You'll be swept to distant lands you've dreamed of visiting . . . . Intrigue, adventure, romance, and the destiny of many lives will thrill you through each Harlequin Presents novel.

 *The very finest
in romantic fiction*

Get all the latest books before they're sold out!

As a Harlequin subscriber you actually receive your
personal copies of the latest Presents novels immediately
after they come off the press, so you're sure of getting all
8 each month.

Cancel your subscription whenever you wish!

You don't have to buy any minimum number of books.
Whenever you decide to stop your subscription just let us
know **and** we'll cancel all further shipments.

Sweet Revenge by **Anne Mather**
Devil in a Silver Room by **Violet Winspear**
Gates of Steel by **Anne Hampson**
No Quarter Asked by **Janet Dailey**